Macmillan McGraw-Hill

Math Connects

2

Chapter 12
Resource Masters

Macmillan/McGraw-Hill

The McGraw·Hill Companies

Macmillan/McGraw-Hill

Send all inquiries to:
Macmillan/McGraw-Hill
8787 Orion Place
Columbus, OH 43240-4027

ISBN: 978-0-02-107234-7
MHID: 0-02-107234-5

Chapter 12 Resource Masters

Printed in the United States of America.

6 7 8 9 10 MAL 16 15 14 13 12 11 10 09

CONTENTS

Teacher's Guide to Using the Chapter 12 Resource Masters

The *Chapter 12 Resource Masters* includes the core materials needed for Chapter 12. These materials include worksheets, extensions, and assessment options. The answers for these pages appear at the back of this booklet.

All of the materials found in this booklet are included for viewing and printing on the *TeacherWorks Plus*™ CD-ROM.

Chapter Resources

Graphic Organizer (page 2) This master is a tool designed to assist students with comprehension of grade-level concepts. You can use this graphic organizer in coordination with the appropriate lesson. While the content and layout of these tools vary, their goal is to assist students by providing a visual representation from which they can learn new concepts.

Student Glossary (page 3) This master is a study tool that presents the key vocabulary terms from the chapter. You may suggest that students highlight or star the terms they do not understand. Give this list to students before beginning Lesson 12-1. Remind them to add these pages to their mathematics study notebooks.

Anticipation Guide (page 4) This is a survey designed for use before beginning the chapter. You can use this survey to highlight what students may or may not know about the concepts in the chapter. If feasible, interview students in small groups, asking them the questions in the guide. There is space for recording how well students answer the questions before they complete the chapter. You may find it helpful to interview students a second time, after completing the chapter, to determine their progress.

Games (page 5) A game is provided to reinforce chapter concerns and may be used at appropriate times throughout the chapter.

Resources for Lessons

Reteach Each lesson has an associated Reteach worksheet. In general, the Reteach worksheet focuses on the same lesson content but uses a different approach, learning style, or modality than that used in the Student Edition. The Reteach worksheet closes with computational practice.

Skills Practice The Skills Practice worksheet for each lesson focuses on the computational aspect of the lesson. The Skills Practice worksheet may be helpful in providing additional practice of the skill taught in the lesson. It also contains word problems that cover the skill. Spaces for students' answers are provided on the worksheet.

Homework Practice The Homework Practice worksheet provides an opportunity for additional computational practice. The Homework Practice worksheet includes word problems that address the skill taught in the lesson. Spaces for students' answers are provided on the worksheet.

Problem-Solving Practice The Problem-Solving Practice worksheet presents additional reinforcement in solving word problems that applies both the concepts of the lesson and some review.

Enrich The Enrich worksheet presents activities that extend the concepts of the lesson or offer a historical or multicultural look at the lesson's concepts. Some enrichment materials are designed to widen students' perspectives on the mathematics they are learning.

Resources for Problem-Solving Lessons In recognition of the importance of problem-solving strategies, worksheets for problem-solving lessons follow a slightly different format. For problem-solving lessons, a two-page Reteach worksheet offers a complete model for choosing a strategy. For each Problem-Solving Strategy lesson, Reteach and Skills Practice worksheets offer reinforcement of the strategy taught in the lesson. In contrast, the Problem-Solving Investigation worksheets include a model strategy on the Reteach worksheets and provide problems requiring several alternate strategies on the practice worksheets.

Assessment Options

The assessment masters in the *Chapter 12 Resource Masters* offer a wide variety of assessment tools for monitoring progress as well as final assessment.

Individual Progress Checklist This checklist explains the chapter's goals or objectives. Teachers can record whether a student's mastery of each objective is beginning (B), developing (D), or mastered (M). The checklist includes space to record notes to parents as well as other pertinent observations.

Chapter Diagnostic Test This one-page test assesses students' grasp of skills that are needed for success in the chapter.

Chapter Pretest This one-page quick check of the chapter's concepts is useful for determining pacing. Performance on the pretest can help you determine which concepts can be covered quickly and which specific concepts may need additional time.

Mid-Chapter Test This one-page chapter test provides an option to assess the first half of the chapter. It includes both multiple-choice and free-response questions.

Vocabulary Test This one-page test focuses on chapter vocabulary. It is suitable for all students. It includes a list of vocabulary words and questions to assess students' knowledge of the words.

Oral Assessment This two-page test consists of one page for teacher directions and questions and a second page for recording responses. Although this assessment is designed to be used with all students, the interview format focuses on assessing chapter content assimilated by ELL students. The variety of approaches includes solving problems using manipulatives as well as pencil and paper.

Listening Assessment This two-page assessment contains one page for teacher directions and one page for responses/recordings. This assessment, too, is suitable for all students but is designed primarily for use with students who may have difficulty reading test materials. The assessment directions progress in difficulty from simple at the beginning of the year to more extensive at the end of the year.

Chapter Project Rubric This one-page rubric is designed for use in assessing the chapter project. You may want to distribute copies of the rubric when you assign the project and use the rubric to record each student's chapter project score.

Chapter Foldables Rubric This one-page rubric is designed to assess the chapter Foldable. It is written to the students, telling them what you will be looking for as you evaluate their completed Foldable.

Leveled Chapter Tests

- *Form 1* assesses basic chapter concepts through multiple-choice questions and is designed for use with below-level students.

- *Form 2A* is designed for on-level students and is primarily for those who may have missed the Form 1 test. It may be used as a retest for students who received additional instruction following the Form 1 test.

- *Form 2B* is designed for students with a below-level command of the English language.

- *Form 2C* is a free-response test designed for on-level students.

- *Form 2D* is written for students with a below-level command of the English language.

Cumulative Test Practice This two-page test, aimed at on-level students, offers a page of multiple-choice questions and a page of free-response questions.

Answers

The answers for the Anticipation Guide and Lesson Resources are provided as reduced pages with answers appearing in black. Full size line-up answer keys are provided for the Assessment Masters.

12

Graphic Organizer

Time Relationships

A suggestion on how to complete this graphic organizer can be found in the answer pages at the back of this book.

Measurements of Classroom Objects		
Paper Clips	Inches	Centimeters

Tell a friend what you learned.

12

Student Glossary

Vocabulary Term	Definition / Description / Example
area	The space inside a shape or figure. [Lesson 12-7] [Example:] The area of this rectangle is 6 square units.
centimeter (cm)	A metric unit of measurement used to find lengths and heights. 0 1 2 3 4 5 6 7 centimeters [Lesson 12-5]
estimate	To find a number close to the exact amount. [Lesson 12-4] Example: 47 + 22 (estimate 50 + 20) is about 70.
inch (in.)	A customary unit for measuring length and height. (plural: inches) 0 1 2 3 inches [Lesson 12-2]
length	How long or how far something is. length [Lesson 12-1]
measure	To find the length, height, weight, capacity, or temperature using standard or nonstandard units. [Lesson 12-1]

Before you begin Chapter 12, distribute the Anticipation Guide to students. Read questions to the students, giving them time to answer each question. You may want to ask the same questions after students complete the chapter.

Before Chapter		After Chapter
	1. What is a better unit of measurement for an eraser: a foot ruler or a paper clip?	
	2. How can you prove that this line is about 1 inch long? ▬▬▬▬▬▬	
	3. Circle the object closest to 12 inches in length.	
	4. This is a centimeter: ▬▬ A single unit cube is about 1 cm. How can knowing this help you guess the length of a base-ten cube?	
	5. What is the area of the figure?	

12

Chapter 12 Game

Measurement Tic-Tac-Toe

Ready

You will need:

4 index cards

markers

2 crayons of different colors

Set

Write one set of the following measurement units on the index cards, one measurement unit per card:

centimeters	inches

Mix the cards and place them facedown on the table. Players choose a circle or an X as their marker.

GO!

1. Player 1 chooses a card and reads the measurement unit.

2. He or she finds an object on the game board that is best measured using that unit. The player then places a circle or an X in that square.

3. Player 1 replaces the card facedown on the table.

4. Each player tries to get three squares in a row, across, down, or diagonally. If players cannot get three in a row, the player with the most squares wins.

Reteach

Nonstandard Units

Different units make different measurements.
A ▢ will give a different measurement than a ⌒
for the same object.

Estimate. Then use ▢ and ⌒ to measure.

1.

about _____ ▢   measure _____ ▢

about _____ ⌒   measure _____ ⌒

2.

about _____ ▢   measure _____ ▢

about _____ ⌒   measure _____ ⌒

3.

about _____ ▢   measure _____ ▢

about _____ ⌒   measure _____ ⌒

6

Name _____

Skills Practice

Nonstandard Units

Find the object. Estimate. Then use 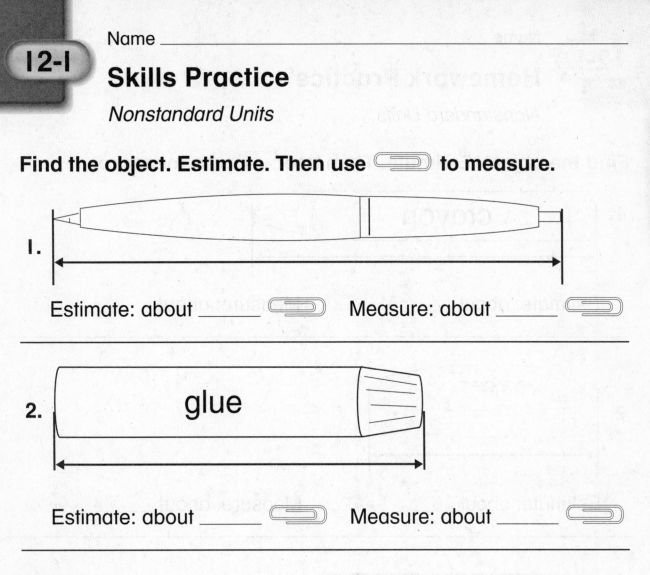 **to measure.**

1.

Estimate: about _____ 🖇   Measure: about _____ 🖇

2.   glue

Estimate: about _____ 🖇   Measure: about _____ 🖇

Solve.

3. Jim wants to measure his marker with cubes and paper clips. About how many of each unit?

about _____ ▢   about _____ 🖇

Are your answers the same or different? Explain why.

_____

_____

Homework Practice

Nonstandard Units

Find the object. Estimate. Then use ⬭ to measure.

1. crayon

Estimate: about _____ ⬭   Measure: about _____ ⬭

2. eraser

Estimate: about _____ ⬭   Measure: about _____ ⬭

3.

Estimate: about _____ ⬭   Measure: about _____ ⬭

4. A ribbon is 30 ⬭ long. Minny cuts off a piece of ribbon about 10 ⬭ long. Write a number sentence to find how much ribbon is left.

_____ ◯ _____ ◯ _____   about _____ ⬭ left

Name _____

Problem-Solving Practice

Nonstandard Units

Solve.

1. A pencil is about 7 ▫ long. A pen is about 9 ▫ long. About how much longer is the pen?

   ___9___ − ___7___ = _____

   The pen is about _____ ▫ longer.

2. A crayon is about 6 ▫ long. A paper clip is about 3 ▫ long. About how much shorter is the paper clip?

   ___6___ − ___3___ = _____

   The paper clip is about _____ ▫ shorter.

3. Kat's red string is about 12 ▫ long. Her blue string is about 8 ▫ long. How do the lengths compare? The blue string is about _____ ▫ shorter.

4. Fred's white straw is about 13 ▫ tall. His green straw is about 16 ▫ tall. About how much taller is Fred's green straw? The green straw is about _____ ▫ taller.

5.

Paper Chain Contest	
Room	Length of Paper Chain
A	
B	
C	

Which room has the longest paper chain? _____

6. A fork is 8 ▫ long. A spoon is 6 ▫ long. A napkin is 9 ▫ long. Write three number sentences that compare the lengths of the napkin, fork, and spoon.

   _____

   _____

12-1

Enrich

Measure Clips

First estimate the length of each line, then measure using paper clips.

1. _____

Estimate: _____   Measure: _____

2.

Estimate: _____   Measure: _____

3.

Estimate: _____   Measure: _____

4. Find 2 objects in your classroom that are 10 paper clips long.

_____

Were your estimates close?   yes   no

5. Write two things that you notice when you use paper clips to measure.

_____

_____

_____

12-2

Reteach

Measure Inches Using Models

Use an inch ruler to measure length.

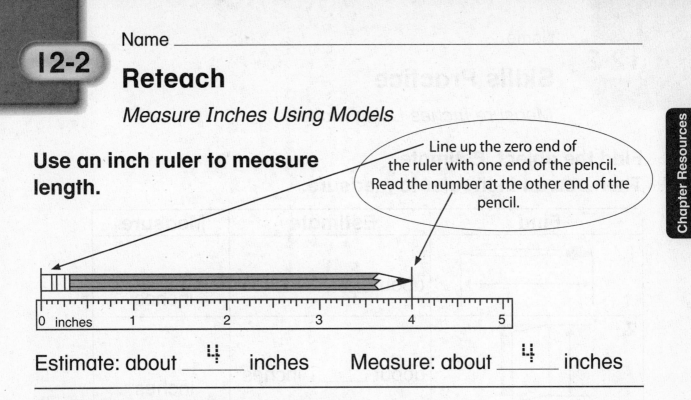

Line up the zero end of the ruler with one end of the pencil. Read the number at the other end of the pencil.

Estimate: about ____4____ inches   Measure: about ____4____ inches

Estimate the length of each picture below.
Then use an inch ruler to measure.

Picture	Estimate	Measure
1. blue crayon	about _____ inches	about _____ inches
2. paper clip	about _____ inches	about _____ inches
3. eraser	about _____ inches	about _____ inches
4. chalk	about _____ inches	about _____ inches
5. stapler	about _____ inches	about _____ inches

Name _____

Skills Practice

Measure Inches Using Models

**Find the object. Estimate.
Then use an inch ruler to measure.**

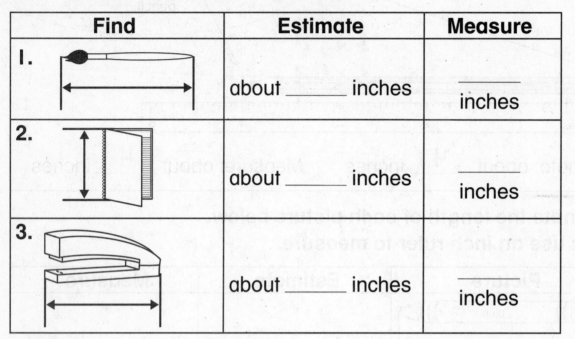

Find	Estimate	Measure
1.	about _____ inches	_____ inches
2.	about _____ inches	_____ inches
3.	about _____ inches	_____ inches

Solve.

4. Ali makes a row of 75¢ in quarters. Each quarter is about one inch long. About how long is Ali's row of quarters? Tell how you know. The row is about _____ inches long.

_____

_____

5. Lu measured one ⬚⬚⬚⬚⬚. It was about 4 inches. She put 3 ⬚⬚⬚⬚⬚ end to end. About how long was the line of three ⬚⬚⬚⬚⬚? Tell how you know.

The line is about _____ inches long.

_____

12

Name _____

Homework Practice

Measure Inches Using Models

Find the object. Estimate.
Then use an inch ruler to measure.

Find	Estimate	Measure
1. book	about _____ inches	_____ inches
2. shoe	about _____ inches	_____ inches
3. marker	about _____ inches	_____ inches

Solve.

4. Six turtles sit in a row. Each turtle is 2 inches wide. About how long is the row of turtles?

   The row is about _____ inches long.

5. Five beetles walk in a line. Each beetle is 3 inches long. About how long is the line of beetles?

   The line is about _____ inches long.

12-2

Problem-Solving Practice

Measure Inches Using Models

Solve.

1. Tom's book is 12 inches long. Nell's birthday card is 7 inches long. How much shorter is the card than the book?

   _____ − _____ = _____   _____ inches shorter

2. Ira measures a flower and a leaf. The flower is 8 inches tall. The leaf is 3 inches tall. How much taller is the flower than the leaf?

   _____ − _____ = _____   _____ inches taller

3. Ken's pencil box is 10 inches long. His pencils are 7 inches long. How much longer is the pencil box than the pencils?

   _____ inches longer

4. Stan's toy train car is 3 inches long. He adds a car. How long is a train of 2 toy train cars?

   _____ inches

5. Paper clips are 2 inches long. Kelly makes a paper clip chain 8 inches long. How many clips does Kelly have?

   _____ paper clips

6. Tony wants to frame a photo. The photo is 5 inches wide and 7 inches tall. He wants the frame to add 2 inches to each side. How big will the frame be?

   _____ inches wide and

   _____ inches tall

Name _____

Enrich

Measureing Around Curves

Measure and cut 12 inches of string. Use the string and ruler to find the length of each curvy line.

1.

Estimate: about _____.

Actual length: _____

2.

Estimate: _____.

Actual length: _____

3.

Estimate: _____.

Actual length: _____

4. Draw a curving line that is about 8 inches long.

Use the string and the ruler to check the length.

12-3

Reteach (1)

Problem-Solving Strategy: Guess and Check

Beth wants to glue this leaf to a card.
The card is 3 inches long.
Will the leaf fit?

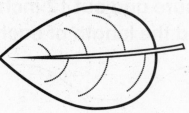

Step 1 **Understand**	**What do I know?** The card is 3 inches long. **What do I need to find?** How long the leaf is.
Step 2 **Plan**	**How will I find the length of the leaf?** I will show 3 inches with three 1 inch ⬭. I will guess by comparing the leaf to the ⬭. Then I will use an inch ruler to check.
Step 3 **Solve**	**Guess and check.** Guess: The leaf is about 1 ⬭ less than the card. I guess that the leaf is __2__ inches long. Check: The leaf is __2__ inches long.
Step 4 **Check**	**Look back.** Was my guess close? _____ Did I answer the question? _____

Name _____

Reteach (2)

Problem-Solving Strategy: Guess and Check

Guess and check to solve.

1. Karen has 4 erasers like this one. She says that if she puts them all in a row, the row will be about 6 inches long. Is she correct? _____

Length of 1 eraser:

Guess: _____   Check: _____ inches

Length of 4 erasers:

Guess: _____   Check: _____ inches

---

2. Marco's pencil is 6 inches long. Is this feather longer or shorter than Marco's pencil? _____

---

3. Ben has 10 paper clips. He says that if he puts them all in a row, the row will be about 10 inches long. Is he correct? _____

Length of 1 paper clip:

Guess: _____   Check: _____ inches

Length of 10 paper clips:

Guess: _____   Check: _____ inches

Name _____

Skills Practice

Problem-Solving Strategy: Guess and Check

Guess and check to solve.

1. Luis wants to break this chalk into 2 equal
pieces. He wants each piece to be 2 inches long.

Is this possible? _____

Guess: _____   Check: _____ inches

2. Jen wants to put this paint brush in a case.
The case is 6 inches long. Will this paint brush

fit in Jen's case? _____

Guess: _____   Check: _____ inches

3. Mike's crayon is 3 paper clips long. Are these
scissors longer or shorter than Mike's crayon? _____

Guess: _____   Check: _____

Name _____

Homework Practice

Problem-Solving Strategy: Guess and Check

Guess and check to solve.

1. Nina wants to glue this row of acorns to a picture. The picture is 6 inches long.

   Will the acorns fit? _____

   Guess: _____   Check: _____ inches

2. Leroy's pet turtle is 2 paper clips long.
   Is this leaf shorter or longer than the turtle? _____

   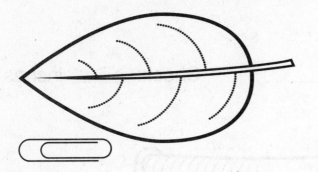

   Guess: _____   Check: _____ ⬭

3. Juan wants to display this shell in a box.
   Can he fit the shell in a 2-inch box? _____

   Guess: _____   Check: _____ inches

Enrich

Up to Bat!

Use the clues to guess length. Use an inch ruler to check your work.

1. Guess: _____   Check: _____ inches

2. Guess: _____   Check: _____ inches

3. Guess: _____   Check: _____ inches

4. Guess: _____   Check: _____ inches

12-4

Reteach

Use an Inch Ruler

You can measure with inches. Use an inch ruler to measure the length or height of objects.

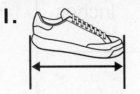

About how tall is the chair?
Circle the better estimate.

about 6 inches

about 24 inches

Think of the real object. Then circle the better estimate.

1.
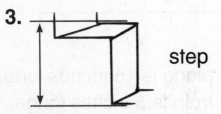

about 5 inches

about 2 feet

2.

about 24 inches

about 7 inches

3.
step

about 7 inches

about 14 inches

4.
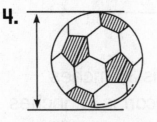

about 9 inches

about 18 inches

Name _____

Skills Practice

Use an Inch Ruler

**Find the object. Use inches.
Estimate. Measure each object in the unit shown.**

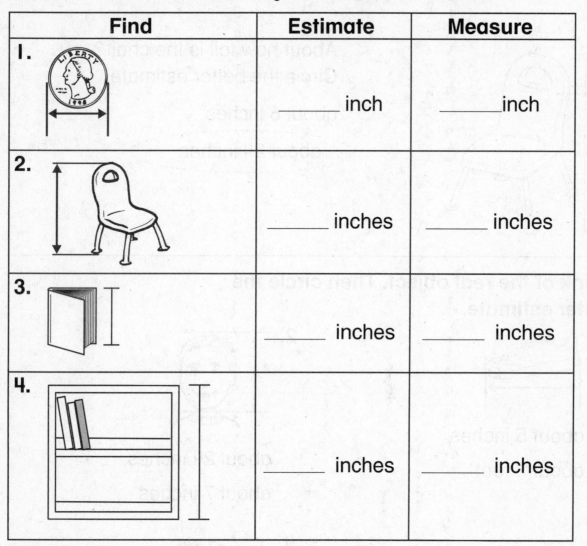

Find	Estimate	Measure
1.	_____ inch	_____ inch
2.	_____ inches	_____ inches
3.	_____ inches	_____ inches
4.	_____ inches	_____ inches

Solve.

5. Lita's scarf is 36 inches long. Jill's scarf is 12 inches shorter. How long is Jill's scarf?

_____ inches long

6. A toy plane is 15 inches long. A toy train is 6 inches longer. How long is the toy train?

_____ inches long

Name _____

Homework Practice

Use an Inch Ruler

Find the object. Use inches.
Estimate. Measure each object in the unit shown.

Find the Object	Estimate	Measure
1.	_____ inch(es)	_____ inch(es)
2.	_____ inches	_____ inches
3.	_____ inches	_____ inches

Solve.

4. Name three things in your classroom that are longer than 1 inch but shorter than 12 inches. Use an inch ruler to measure.

_____

_____

5. Name three things in your classroom that are longer than 12 inches. Use an inch ruler to measure.

_____

_____

12-4

Problem-Solving Practice

Use an Inch Ruler

Solve.

1 foot = 12 inches
1 yard = 3 feet

1. Ann's dad gave her a 24-inch doll and a 36-inch bat. How much longer is the bat?

   _____ inches

2. Nate's baby snake is 7 inches long. It grows to 36 inches. How much did the snake grow?

   _____ inches

3. Mr. Ryan's class planted a 9-inch tall tree. It is now 48 inches tall. How many inches did it grow?

   _____ inches

4. Rosa's poster is 12 inches long. Pat's poster is 14 inches long. How long are their posters together?

   _____ inches

5. Jake draws a line that is 72 inches long. Ted draws a line that is 8 inches longer. How long is Ted's line?

   _____ inches

6. Ms. Li's class has a fish tank that is 42 inches long. Mr. Kent's class tank is 30 inches long. How much longer is Ms. Li's class tank?

   _____ inches

12-4

Enrich

Use an Inch Ruler

Play this game with a partner. Cut out the cards at the bottom of the page to play.

How to Play

- A player picks one card and estimates the object.

- The other player uses a ruler to find the actual measurement.

- If the estimate is close to the actual measurement, the first player gets a point.

- Continue taking turns until a player gets 10 points.

a book	chair leg	paper clip	table leg
supply box	stapler	chalk	eraser
a shoe	crayon	pencil	door

Name _____

Reteach

Measure Centimeters Using Models

Use the centimeter ruler to measure.

> Line up the zero end of the ruler with one end of the crayon. Read the number at the other end of the crayon.

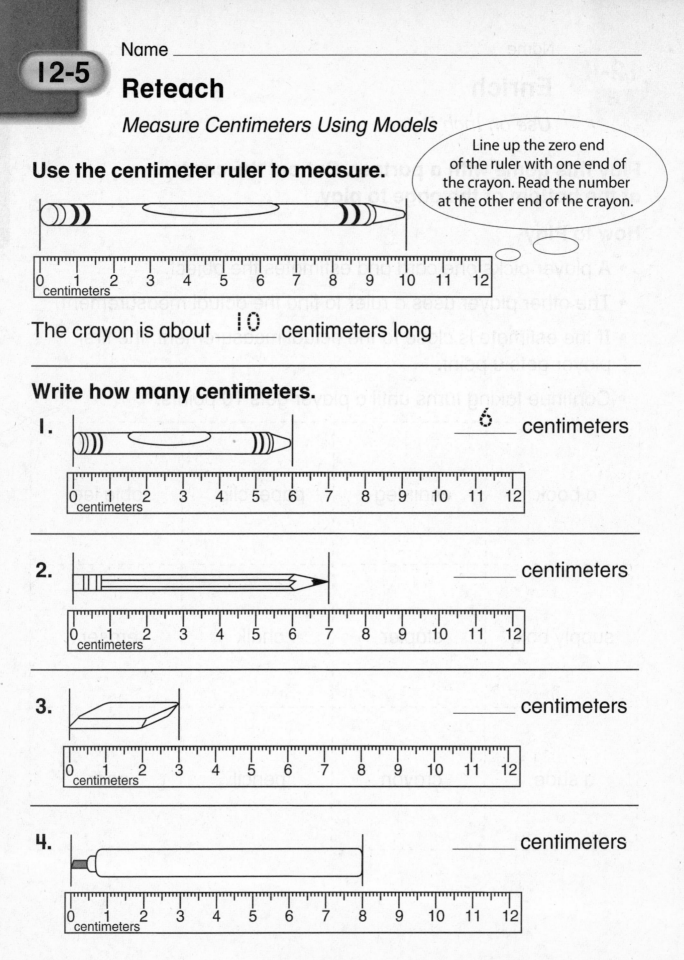

The crayon is about ____10____ centimeters long

Write how many centimeters.

1. ____6____ centimeters

2. _____ centimeters

3. _____ centimeters

4. _____ centimeters

Name _____

Skills Practice

Measure Centimeters Using Models

Use a centimeter ruler to measure.

Line up the zero end of the ruler with one end of the crayon. Read the number at the other end of the crayon.

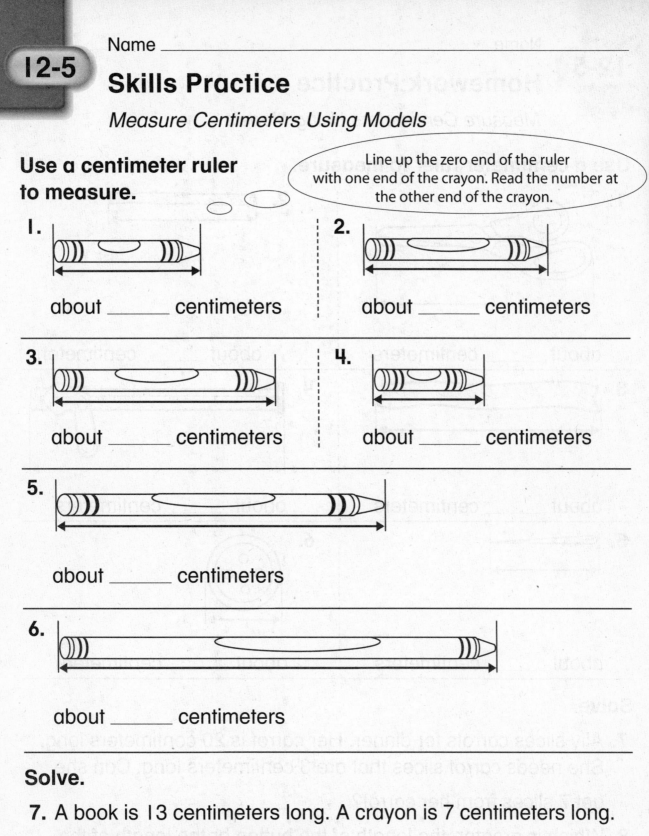

1.

about _____ centimeters

2.

about _____ centimeters

3.

about _____ centimeters

4.

about _____ centimeters

5.

about _____ centimeters

6.

about _____ centimeters

Solve.

7. A book is 13 centimeters long. A crayon is 7 centimeters long. How much longer is the book?

   The book is _____ centimeters longer.

Name _____

Homework Practice

Measure Centimeters Using Models

Use a centimeter ruler to measure.

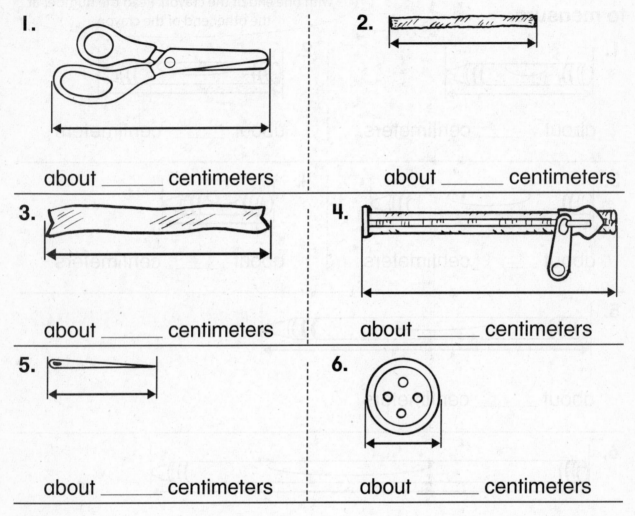

1.

about _____ centimeters

2.

about _____ centimeters

3.

about _____ centimeters

4.

about _____ centimeters

5.

about _____ centimeters

6.

about _____ centimeters

Solve.

7. Ally slices carrots for dinner. Her carrot is 20 centimeters long. She needs carrot slices that are 3 centimeters long. Can she get 7 slices from her carrot? _____

8. Which is greater, the length of the button or the length of the needle? _____

12-5

Problem-Solving Practice

Measure Centimeters Using Models

Solve.

1. Kira is making a clay snake. Yesterday, it was 23 centimeters long. Today, it is 49 centimeters long. How many centimeters did Kira add?

_____ centimeters

2. Stan has a paper chain that is 60 centimeters long. He adds 15 centimeters of paper to it. How long is the paper chain now?

_____ centimeters

3. Cho makes a row of 23 pennies. Each penny is about 2 centimeters wide. About how long is Cho's row?

The row is about _____ centimeters long.

4. Ty makes a paper clip chain that is 50 centimeters long. There are 10 paper clips in the chain. About how long is each paper clip?

Each clip is about _____ centimeters long.

5. Ramon is making a comic strip. His paper is 24 centimeters wide. He draws panels that are 8 centimeters wide. How many panels does Ramon have?

_____ panels

6. Elena is drawing a border around a square picture. Each side of the border is 10 centimeters long. How many total centimeters will the border be?

_____ centimeters

Name _____

Enrich

How Big is a Bug?

Use your little finger to estimate length. Then cut out the centimeter ruler and use it to find the actual length.

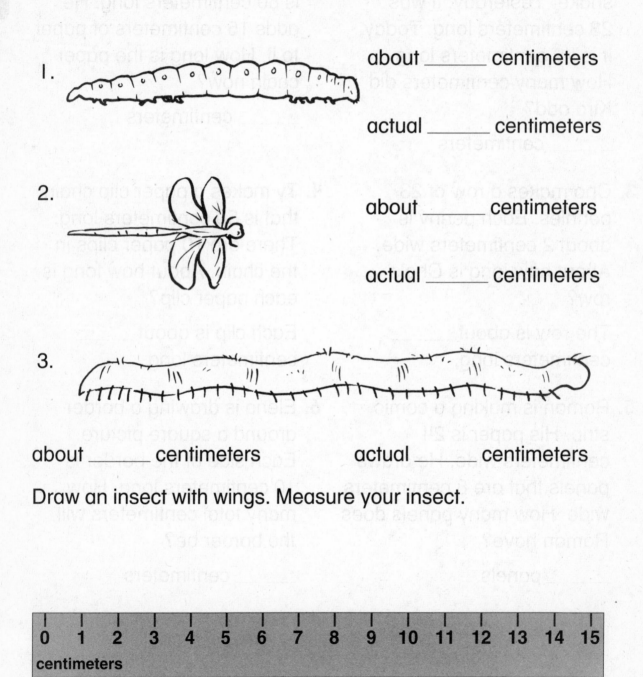

1.

about _____ centimeters

actual _____ centimeters

2.

about _____ centimeters

actual _____ centimeters

3.

about _____ centimeters   actual _____ centimeters

Draw an insect with wings. Measure your insect.

```
 |   |   |   |   |   |   |   |   |   |   |   |   |   |   |   |
 0   1   2   3   4   5   6   7   8   9  10  11  12  13  14  15
centimeters
```

Name _____

Reteach

Use a Centimeter Ruler

You can measure with centimeters. Use a centimeter ruler to measure the length or height of objects.

Estimate: about _____ centimeters

Measure: about _____ centimeters

Estimate. Find an object for each length.

Estimate	Object	Measure
1. about 10 centimeters	_____	_____ centimeters
2. about 20 centimeters	_____	_____ centimeters
3. about 30 centimeters	_____	_____ centimeters
4. about 40 centimeters	_____	_____ centimeters

Name _____

Skills Practice

Use a Centimeter Ruler

Find the object. Estimate. Measure each object in centimeters.

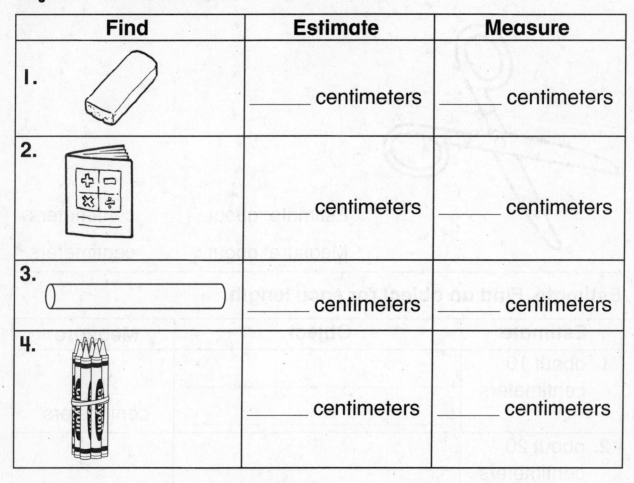

Find	Estimate	Measure
1.	_____ centimeters	_____ centimeters
2.	_____ centimeters	_____ centimeters
3.	_____ centimeters	_____ centimeters
4.	_____ centimeters	_____ centimeters

5. Name three things in your classroom that are longer than 25 centimeters but shorter than 50 centimeters. Use a centimeter ruler to measure them.

_____

6. Name two things in your classroom that are longer than 50 centimeters. Use a centimeter ruler to measure them.

_____

32

Name _____

Homework Practice

Use a Centimeter Ruler

Find the object. Estimate. Measure each item in centimeters.

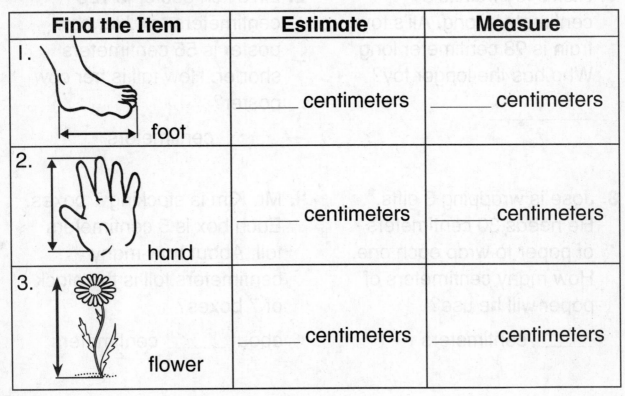

Find the Item	Estimate	Measure
1. foot	_____ centimeters	_____ centimeters
2. hand	_____ centimeters	_____ centimeters
3. flower	_____ centimeters	_____ centimeters

Solve.

4. Kal needs two 50-centimeter pieces of cloth. Can he cut what he needs from a 100-centimeter length of cloth? _____

5. Name three things in your home that are longer than 100 centimeters.

_____

6. Name three things in your home that are shorter than 100 centimeters.

_____

12-6

Problem-Solving Practice

Use a Centimeter Ruler

Solve.

1. Rick's toy train is 89 centimeters long. Ali's toy train is 98 centimeter long. Who has the longer toy?

   _____

2. Lin's fish poster is 125 centimeters tall. Her cow poster is 55 centimeters shorter. How tall is her cow poster?

   _____ centimeters

3. Jose is wrapping 3 gifts. He needs 30 centimeters of paper to wrap each one. How many centimeters of paper will he use?

   _____ centimeters

4. Mr. Kim is stacking 7 boxes. Each box is 5 centimeters tall. About how many centimeters tall is the stack of 7 boxes?

   about _____ centimeters

5. A stack of 5 nickels is about 1 centimeter tall. Cass puts her nickels in a stack. Her stack is about 16 centimeters tall. How many nickels does Cass have?

   She has _____ nickels.

6. Andre measures one penny. It is 2 centimeters wide. Next, Andre puts all his pennies in a row. The row is 64 centimeters long. How many pennies does Andre have?

   Andre has _____ pennies.

12-6

Enrich

Measuring Me

Use the string to measure. Lay the string on the centimeter ruler to find the actual length. Record your answers.

Did you know?
Your height should be about the same distance as your arm span.

1. Your height: estimate _____   actual _____

Hold your arms out like a bird. Measure your arm span, the distance from one fingertip to the other:

estimate _____   actual _____

Did you know?
The length of your foot is about the same as the distance between your elbow and your wrist.

2. The length of your foot: estimate _____   actual _____

The distance between your elbow and your wrist:

estimate _____   actual _____

Do you think that centimeters are a good choice to use when measuring your height? Give a reason for your answer.

_____

Name _____

Reteach

Understanding Area

Area is the number of square units it takes to cover a space.
Color squares to create shapes with the given areas.

1. 5 square units

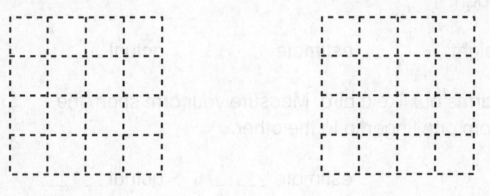

2. 7 square units

_____

_____

3. 10 square units

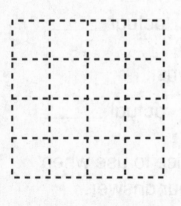

4. 11 square units

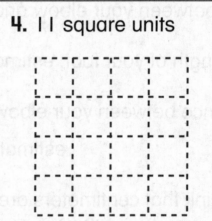

_____

_____

12-7

Skills Practice

Understanding Area

Count **to find the area.**

1.

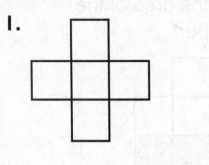

_____ square units

2.

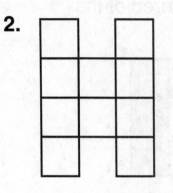

_____ square units

3.

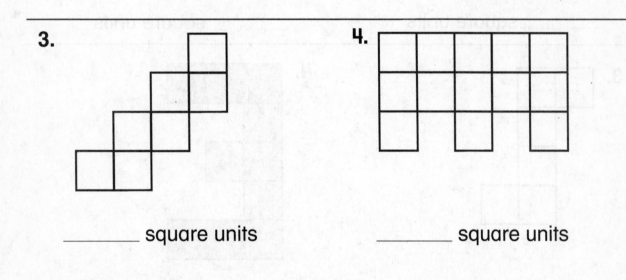

_____ square units

4.

_____ square units

5. Rob used white and gray pattern blocks to make this shape. What is the area of the gray part?

_____ square units

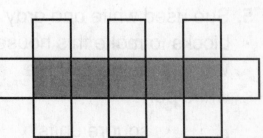

Name _____

Homework Practice

Understanding Area

Count ☐ **to find the area.**

1. Find the area of the gray part.

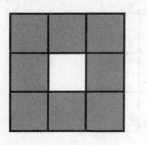

_____ square units

2. Find the area of the gray part.

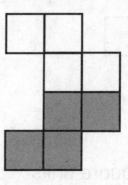

_____ square units

3.

_____ square units

4.

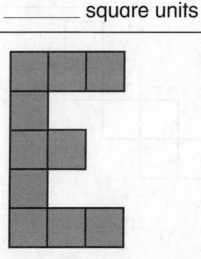

_____ square units

5. Sue used white and gray blocks to make this house. What is the area of the white part?

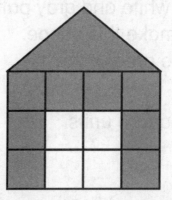

_____ square units

38

Name _____

Problem-Solving Practice

Understanding Area

Find the area to solve.

1. Eve made this shape out of blocks. What is the area of Eve's shape?

   _____ square units

2. Pablo used blocks to show the letter F. What is the area of Pablo's F?

   _____ square units

3. Lexi made this bridge out of sugar cubes. What is the area of Lexi's bridge?

   _____ square units

4. Sam used sugar cubes to make this shape. What is the area of Sam's shape?

   _____ square units

Enrich

Apple Area

Use the key to color the squares. Then, count to find the area of each color.

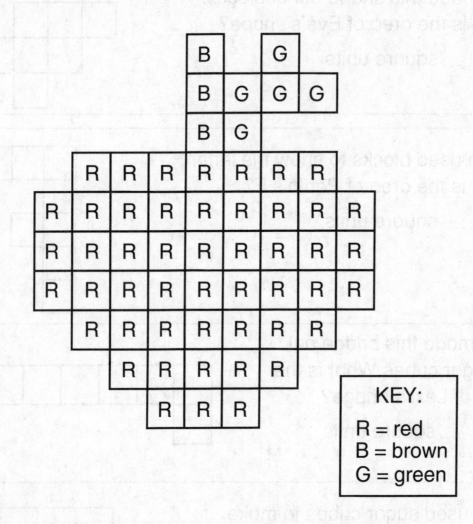

KEY:

R = red
B = brown
G = green

The area of the **red** part is _____ square units.

The area of the **brown** part is _____ square units.

The area of the **green** part is _____ square units.

12-8

Reteach

Problem-Solving Investigation: Choose a Strategy

Kim buys 10 inches of animal stickers. Each sticker is 2 inches long. How many stickers does Kim buy?

Step 1 **Understand**	**What do you know?** • Kim buys ___10___ inches of stickers. • One sticker is ___2___ inches long. **What do you need to find?** • How many stickers are in _____ inches.
Step 2 **Plan**	**How will I find have many stickers Kim buys?** Find the number of stickers in two inches. Then make a table to show the number of stickers in _____ inches.
Step 3 **Solve**	**Make a table.**

inches	2	4	6	8	10
stickers	1	2	3	4	5

This means there are ___5___ stickers in 10 inches.

Step 4 **Check**	**Look back.** Check to see if your solution is reasonable. Read the problem again. Does your table answer the question? yes no

Name _____

Reteach (2)

Problem-Solving Investigation: Choose a Strategy

Choose a strategy to solve.

- Make a table
- Draw a picture
- Use logical reasoning

1. Ms. Jones needs 72 inches of ribbon for the class party. One roll of ribbon is 24 inches long. How many rolls does Ms. Jones need? _____ rolls

rolls			
yards of ribbon			

2. Mr. Karr is putting up new curtains. The window is 120 inches wide. His curtains are 30 inches wide. How many curtains are needed to cover the window?

_____ curtains

curtains			
inches of curtain			

3. Vic and his dad are painting a chess board. The board is 8 squares across. Each square is 3 inches wide. How many inches wide is the whole board? _____ inches

4. Mary's mom is painting her bedroom wall. About one can of paint covers an area that is 48 inches high and 60 inches long. Mary's wall is 96 inches high and 120 inches long. Are 2 cans of paint enough?

Name _____

Skills Practice

Problem-Solving Investigation: Choose a Strategy

Chapter Resources

Choose a strategy to solve.

- Make a table • Draw a picture • Use logical reasoning

1. Jane wants to build a block tower that is 40 inches high. Each block is 2 inches high. How many blocks does she need?

    _____ blocks

2. Koto is hanging 36-inch curtains. The window is 72 inches wide. How many curtains are needed to cover the window?

    _____ curtains

3. Jamal draws a picture that is 22 inches long and 22 inches wide. He wants to put a ribbon border on it. About how many inches of ribbon does he need?

    _____ inches

4. Tina's mom is sewing an American flag. There are 13 stripes. They are 2 inches wide. How many inches wide is the flag?

    _____ inches

5. Tim measures his shoe. It is 6 inches long. Then, he walks across a room. He put the heel of his right shoe against the toe of the left shoe. He says the room is about 20 shoes long. About how long is the room in inches?

    _____ inches

12-8

Homework Practice

Problem-Solving Investigation: Choose a Strategy

Choose a strategy to solve.

- Make a table   • Draw a picture   • Use logical reasoning

1. Ms. Barnes is stacking 8 boxes. Each box is 15 centimeters high. How many centimeters high is Ms. Barnes' stack of boxes?

    _____ centimeters

2. Mika bought 15 inches of heart stickers. Each sticker is 3 inches long. How many stickers did Mika buy?

    _____ stickers

3. Evan's picture is 55 centimeters long and 10 centimeters wide. He wants to make a yarn border. How many centimeters of yarn does Evan need? (Hint: Remember, there are 4 sides to a picture.)

    _____ centimeters

4.  Farmer Ben's pony is 9 hands tall. I hand is 4 inches. About how tall is the pony in inches?

    _____ inches

Name _____

Enrich

Logical Length

Abner, Beth, Celia and Danny put their pencils in a can on the table. Use the clues and a ruler. Draw lines that show how long each pencil is, then answer the questions.

Clues:

1. Abner's pencil is 4 inches long.

2. Beth's pencil is 1 inch shorter than Celia's pencil.

3. Celia's pencil is 2 inches longer than Abner's pencil.

4. Danny's pencil is the same length as Beth's pencil.

How long is each pencil?

Abner _____ inches

Beth _____ inches

Celia _____ inches

Danny _____ inches

Name _____

Individual Progress Checklist

Learning Mastery			Lesson	Lesson Goal	Comments
B	D	M			
			12-1	Estimate and measure length using nonstandard units.	
			12-2	Estimate and measure length using inches.	
			12-3	Guess and check to solve problems.	
			12-4	Estimate and measure length using inches.	
			12-5	Estimate and measure length using centimeters.	
			12-6	Estimate and measure to the nearest centimeter.	
			12-7	Use non-standard units to find the area of shapes.	
			12-8	Choose a strategy to solve problems.	

B = Beginning; **D** = Developing; **M** = Mastered

Note to Parents

_____

_____

_____

_____

_____

_____

_____

Chapter Diagnostic Test

Are You Ready For Chapter 12?

Write the length.

1.

_____

2.
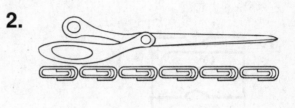
_____

Circle the better estimate.

3.   CD

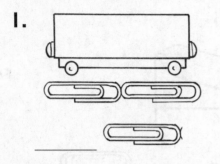

about 2 inches

about 5 inches

about 15 inches

4.   paint brush

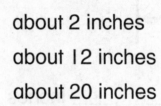

about 2 inches

about 12 inches

about 20 inches

Circle the number of squares in the shape.

5.
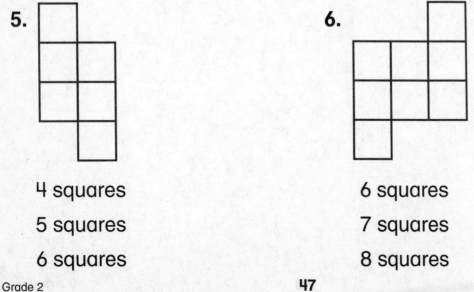

4 squares

5 squares

6 squares

6.

6 squares

7 squares

8 squares

12 **Chapter Pretest**

Find the objects. Estimate the length. Measure using 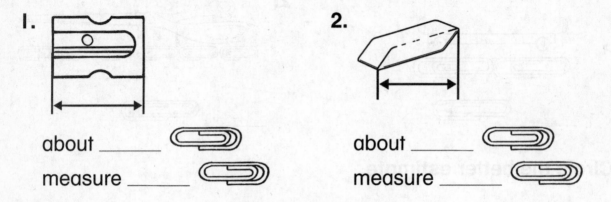.

1.

about _____

measure _____

2.

about _____

measure _____

Find the objects. Estimate the length and measure.

3.

about _____ inches

measure _____ inches

4.

about _____ inches

measure _____ inches

Mid-Chapter Test

Estimate. Measure to the nearest centimeter or inch.

Find the Object	Estimate	Measure
1.	about _____ centimeters	_____ centimeters
2. pencil	about _____ inches	_____ inches
3. paint brush	about _____ centimeters	_____ centimeters
4. CD	about _____ inches	_____ inches
5.	about _____ centimeters	_____ centimeters

Name _____

Vocabulary Test

Use the words in the word bank.
Write the correct word in the blank.

area
estimate
measure
length
inch
inches
centimeter

1. A customary unit for measuring
   length is an _____.

2. Metric units for measuring length
   are _____.

3. When you use a standard unit to find
   the length or height of an object
   you _____.

4. The number of units an object is long is the object's
   _____.

5. When you round 22 inches to 20 inches, you
   _____.

6. _____ is the space inside a shape.

Name _____

Oral Assessment

Preparation: The following classroom objects are needed for this assessment: connecting cubes, paper clips, a stick of chalk, a flat pink eraser, a marker, and a pencil. Board access is required. An inch ruler and a centimeter ruler are required to measure.

Directions: This test targets those students who have developing verbal skills—both oral and written. Ask the questions below and have students record their answers, or record the answers they supply.

1. Give students several small paper clips, a stick of chalk, and a flat pink eraser. Ask, *How many paper clips would you need to measure this piece of chalk? How many would you need for this marker?*

2. Have students measure both objects using paper clips as a standard of measure. If estimates and actual measurements are significantly different, ask, *Why do you think your estimate and the actual measurement are different?*

3. Give students an inch ruler and a marker and pencil. Ask, *How many inches long do you think this marker is? How about this pencil?*

4. Have students measure both objects using the inch ruler. After they measure, ask, *Did your estimate match the measurement?*

5. On the board, draw a square divided into 9 equal units. Tell students to model the square with connecting cubes. Ask, *What is the area of the this square?*

6. Have students measure one of their connecting cubes with a centimeter ruler. Ask, *How many centimeters is the cube?*

7. Have students look at their pinky fingers. Ask, *How many centimeters long do you think your pinky finger is?* After they estimate, have them measure their pinky fingers and record the results.

Notes and comments

_____

_____

_____

_____

_____

Name _____

Oral Assessment Response Sheet

1. _____

2. _____

3. _____

4. _____

5. _____

6. _____

7. _____

8. _____

Name _____

Listening Assessment

Preparation: Paper clips, crayons, sticky notes, and base-ten cubes are needed for this assessment. An inch ruler, a centimeter ruler, and a yardstick are required for measuring.

Directions: Ask students to complete each of the following groups of tasks.

1. Estimate the length, in paper clips, of a crayon.
   Estimate the length, in paper clips, of a small pad of sticky notes.
   Measure the length of the crayon.
   Measure the length of the sticky notes.

2. Study an inch ruler.
   Estimate the length, in paper clips, of a crayon.
   Describe how to use the ruler to measure the length of an object.
   Measure the length of a crayon.

3. Study a centimeter ruler.
   Estimate the length, in centimeters, of a base-ten cube.
   Measure the base-ten cube.
   Record the measurements in centimeters.

4. Draw a square.
   Divide the square into 9 equal units.
   Number the units.
   Circle the word that applies to these units.

Notes

_____

_____

_____

_____

Name _____

Listening Assessment Response Sheet

1. _____   **2.** _____

_____   _____

_____   _____

_____   _____

_____

3. _____   **4.**

_____

_____

_____   _____ units

_____

                                         area   length

Chapter Project Rubric

Score	Explanation
3	Student successfully measured everyday objects and recorded those measurements. Student chose an object, recorded an estimate, measured it using the appropriate unit, and recorded the measurement and the unit it was measured with. Student used a detailed and accurate chart for his or her recordings. Student correctly listed all of the objects measured from smallest to largest.
2	Student successfully measured everyday objects and recorded those measurements. Student chose an object, recorded an estimate, measured it, and recorded the measurement and the unit it was measured with. Student correctly listed all of the objects measured from smallest to largest.
1	Student measured everyday objects and recorded those measurements. Student chose an object, measured it, and recorded the measurement and the unit it was measured with. Student incorrectly listed the objects from smallest to largest.
0	Student did not successfully participate in this task. Student either did not measure the objects or measured them incorrectly.

Name _____

Chapter Foldables Rubric

Score	Explanation
3	Student successfully made and used the chapter Foldables to record measurements of length.
	Student measured the length of objects using standard and nonstandard units, and was able to describe objects in terms of inches, feet, centimeters, meters, and yards.
2	Student successfully made and used the chapter Foldables to record measurements of length.
	Student measured the length of objects using standard and nonstandard units.
1	Student successfully made and used the chapter Foldables to record measurements of length and time.
	Student measured the length of objects using standard and nonstandard units.
0	Student did not successfully construct or use the chapter Foldables to record measurements of length.
	Student did not correctly apply standard and nonstandard units when measuring length.

Chapter Test, Form I

Read each question carefully.
Fill in the circle for the correct answer.

1. Use a centimeter ruler to measure. How long is the arrow?

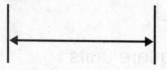

- ○ 6 cm
- ○ 5 cm
- ○ 4 cm
- ○ 3 cm

2. How long is the arrow? Use an inch ruler to measure.

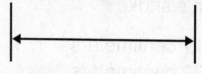

- ○ I inch
- ○ 2 inches
- ○ 3 inches
- ○ 4 inches

3. Which object is about I inch long?

- ○ eraser
- ○ calculator
- ○ desk top
- ○ pencil

4. About how many inches long is your pencil?

- ○ 6 inches
- ○ 12 inches
- ○ 24 inches
- ○ 36 inches

5.

What unit of measure would you use to measure the object?

- ○ pounds
- ○ inches
- ○ cups
- ○ gallons

GO ON

6. Holly's clay snake is 24 centimeters long. Sam's clay snake is 45 centimeters long. How much longer is Sam's snake?

○ 19 centimeters
○ 20 centimeters
○ 21 centimeters
○ 69 centimeters

7. What is the area of the shape?

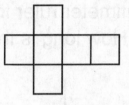

○ 6 square units
○ 7 square units
○ 8 square units
○ 9 square units

8. What is the area of the shape?

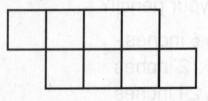

○ 7 square units
○ 8 square units
○ 9 square units
○ 10 square units

9. Ray wants to know if his crayon can fit in a box that is 4 inches long. How can he solve this problem?

○ Act it out
○ Draw a picture
○ Make a table
○ Guess and check

10. About how many paper clips long is the chalk?

○ 5
○ 6
○ 7
○ 8

Name _____

Chapter Test, Form 2A

Read each question carefully.
Darken the circle for the correct answer.

1. How long is this CD case using the paper clip as a unit of measure?

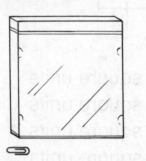

○ about 2 paper clips
○ about 3 paper clips
○ about 4 paper clips
○ about 5 paper clips

2. How long is the arrow? Use an inch ruler to measure the arrow.

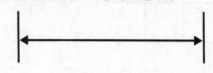

○ 1 inch
○ 2 inches
○ 3 inches
○ 4 inches

3. Which object is about 1 inch long?

○ eraser
○ a math book
○ desk top
○ pencil

4. Which object is about 2 centimeters long?

○ computer
○ crayon
○ notebook paper
○ a paper clip

5. What is the area of the shape?

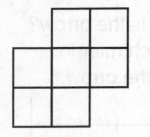

- ○ 7 square units
- ○ 8 square units
- ○ 9 square units
- ○ 14 square units

6. What is the area of the shape?

- ○ 6 square units
- ○ 7 square units
- ○ 8 square units
- ○ 9 square units

7. Katie's blue scarf is 55 centimeters long. Her red scarf is 80 centimeters long. How much longer is the red scarf?

- ○ 25 centimeters
- ○ 50 centimeters
- ○ 30 centimeters
- ○ 135 centimeters

8. Lauren wants to know if her hat can fit on a shelf that is 12 inches long. How can she solve this problem?

- ○ Use logical reasoning
- ○ Guess and check
- ○ Make a table
- ○ Act it out

9. About how many paper clips long is the rug?

- ○ 3
- ○ 4
- ○ 5
- ○ 6

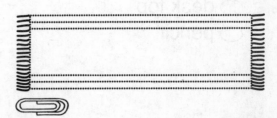

STOP

Name _____

Chapter Test, Form 2B

Read each question carefully.
Fill in the circle for the correct answer.

1. How many paper clips wide is this book?

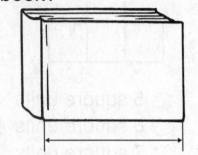

○ about 10 paper clips
○ about 6 paper clips
○ about 3 paper clips

2. How long is the arrow? Use an inch ruler.

○ 3 inches
○ 2 inches
○ 1 inch

3. About how wide is this cherry?

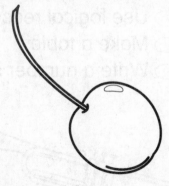

○ 1 inch
○ 10 inches
○ 100 inches

4. A window is 12 inches long. How many inches are there in 2 windows?

○ 6 inches
○ 24 inches
○ 36 inches

5. What is the area of the shape?

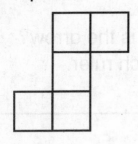

- ◯ 4 square units
- ◯ 5 square units
- ◯ 6 square units
- ◯ 7 square units

6. What is the area of the shape?

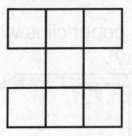

- ◯ 5 square units
- ◯ 6 square units
- ◯ 7 square units
- ◯ 8 square units

7. Nat's floor lamp is 65 centimeters tall. His desk lamp is 30 centimeters tall. How much taller is the floor lamp?

- ◯ 20 centimeters
- ◯ 25 centimeters
- ◯ 30 centimeters
- ◯ 35 centimeters

8. Jose wants to know if his scissors can fit in a desk drawer that is 9 inches wide. How can he solve this problem?

- ◯ Guess and check
- ◯ Use logical reasoning
- ◯ Make a table
- ◯ Write a number senence

9. About how many paper clips long is the trumpet?

- ◯ 5
- ◯ 6
- ◯ 7
- ◯ 8

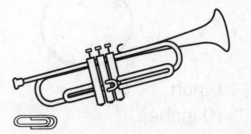

STOP

Name _____

Chapter Test, Form 2C

Read each question carefully.
Write or circle your answer in the space provided.

1. How wide is this book using the paper clip as a unit of measure?

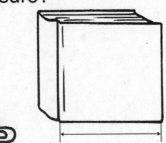

about _____ paper clips

2. How long is the arrow? Use an inch ruler to measure.

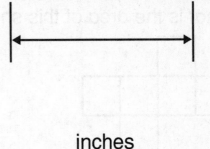

_____ inches

3. Circle the correct unit. An eraser is about _____ wide.

1 inch   10 inches   100 inches

4. Ann's book is 12 inches wide. How many inches wide are 3 of these books?

_____ inches

5. How long is the arrow? Use a centimeter ruler to measure.

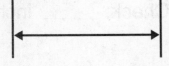

_____ centimeters

6. Maria's block tower is 36 centimeters tall. Brian's block tower is 13 centimeters tall. If they combine towers, how tall will it be?

_____ centimeters

7. What is the area of this shape?

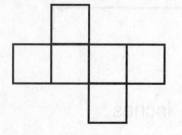

_____ square units

8. What is the area of the gray part?

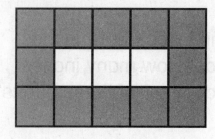

_____ square units

9. Jan wants to put this pencil in a 5-inch box. Can it fit?

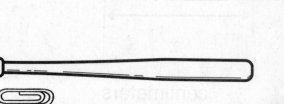

Guess: _____   Check: _____ inches

10. About how many paper clips long is this bat?

_____

STOP

Read each question carefully.
Write or circle your answer in the space provided.

1. How many paper clips wide is this book?

about _____ paper clips

2. How long is the arrow? Use an inch ruler to measure.

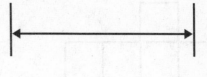

_____ inches

3. Circle the correct unit. How long is this sheet of paper?

about an inch

about 12 inches

about 24 inches

4. Ann's book is 10 inches wide. How wide are 3 books?

_____ inches

5. How long is the arrow?
Use a centimeter ruler to measure.

_____ centimeters

Name _____

6. Maria's block tower is 36 centimeters tall.
Brian's block tower is 12 centimeters tall.
How tall are they together?

_____ centimeters

7. What is the area of this shape?

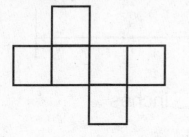

_____ square units

8. What is the area of the gray part?

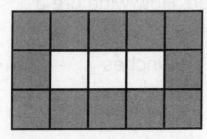

_____ square units

9. Jan wants to put this pencil in a
5-inch box. Can it fit?

Guess: _____

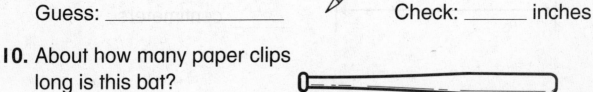

Check: _____ inches

10. About how many paper clips
long is this bat?

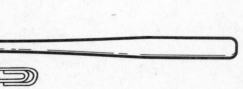

_____

STOP

Read each question carefully.
Fill in the circle for the correct answer.

1. Josh finds 17 seashells on the beach. He gives 6 of them to his sister. How many seashells does Josh have left?

- ◯ 6
- ◯ 11
- ◯ 12
- ◯ 23

2. $400 + 70 + 4$
Which is a different way to show the number?

- ◯ 40 hundreds 7 tens 4 ones
- ◯ $400 + 7 + 4$
- ◯ four hundred seventy-four
- ◯ four seventy and four

3. Eliot has 4 pencils. Marco has 5 pencils. Lavonne has 6 pencils. How many pencils in all?

- ◯ 15 pencils
- ◯ 14 pencils
- ◯ 10 pencils
- ◯ 3 pencils

4. Justin makes 20 free throws. Tommy makes 17 free throws. Brian makes 14 free throws. How many free throws do they make in all?

- ◯ 11
- ◯ 41
- ◯ 45
- ◯ 51

Name _____

Cumulative Test Practice (continued)

Read each question carefully.
Write your answer on the line.

5. 34
   − 6

6.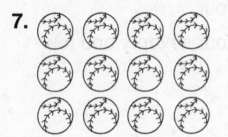

   How many cents? _____ ¢

7.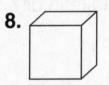

   Count how many baseball there are. Write the answer as a number and number name.

   _____

8.

   How many faces does this figure have?

   _____

9. A lunch box is 12 inches long. How many inches are in 4 lunch boxes?

   _____

Answers (Graphic Organizer and Anticipation Guide)

Graphic Organizer (page 2)

Name _____

12 Graphic Organizer

Time Relationships

A suggestion on how to complete this graphic organizer can be found in the answer pages at the back of this book.

Measurements of Classroom Objects		
Paper Clips	Inches	Centimeters
Answers will vary.	Answers will vary.	Answers will vary.
Answers will vary.	Answers will vary.	Answers will vary.
Answers will vary.	Answers will vary.	Answers will vary.
Answers will vary.	Answers will vary.	Answers will vary.

Tell a friend what you learned.

Note to Teacher: You may use this graphic organizer to help students keep track of different measurements of the same objects. By illustrating that an object's measurement depends on what units it is measured in, you will reinforce the differences between these units. Pick a simple classroom object and have students measure it in paper clips, inches, and centimeters. Help them record the measurements in the three-column chart. Repeat the activity with other classroom objects.

Anticipation Guide (page 4)

Name _____

12 Anticipation Guide

Before you begin Chapter 12, distribute the Anticipation Guide to students. Read questions to the students, giving them time to answer each question. You may want to ask the same questions after students complete the chapter.

	Before Chapter	After Chapter
1. What is a better unit of measurement for an eraser: a foot ruler or a paper clip?		a paper clip
2. How can you prove that this line is about 1 inch long? _____		Use an inch ruler to measure the line.
3. Circle the object closest to 12 inches in length.		
4. This is a centimeter: _____ A single unit cube is about 1 cm. How can knowing this help you guess the length of a base-ten cube?		If one cube is 1 cm, 10 cubes must be 10 cm.
5. What is the area of the figure?		6 square units

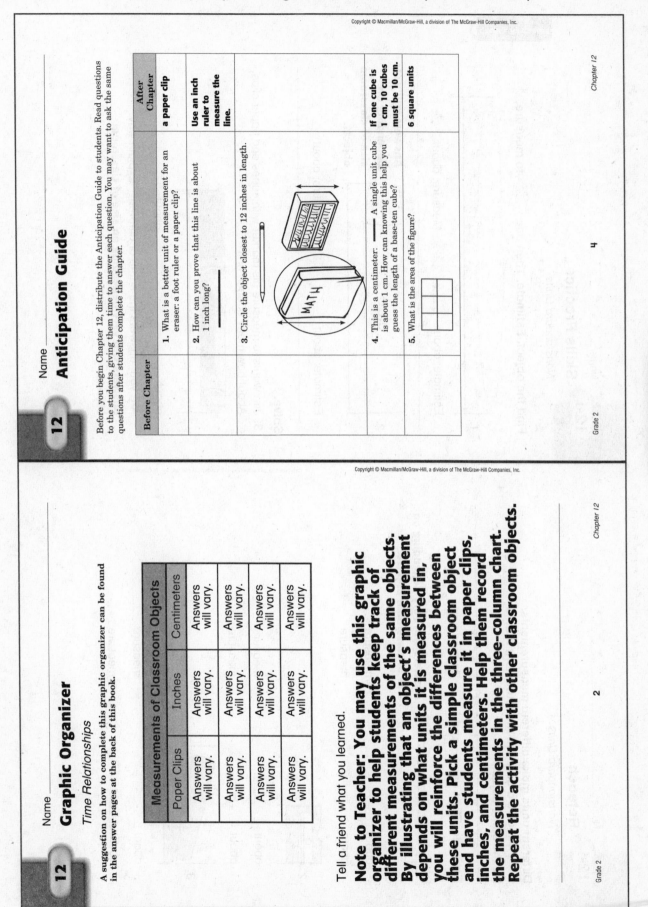

Answers

Answers (Lesson 12-1)

12-1

Name

Skills Practice
Nonstandard Units

Find the object. Estimate. Then use 🖇 to measure.

1.
Estimate: about _____ Measure: about _____

2.
glue
Answers will vary depending on size of classroom objects.
Estimate: about _____ Measure: about _____

Solve.

3. Jim wants to measure his marker with cubes and paper clips. About how many of each unit?

about _____ about _____

Are your answers the same or different? Explain why.
Answers will vary depending on size of classroom objects.

12-1

Name

Reteach
Nonstandard Units

**Different units make different measurements.
A 🔲 will give a different measurement than a 🖇 for the same object.**

Estimate. Then use 🔲 and 🖇 to measure.

Answers will vary depending on size of classroom objects.

1.
about _____ measure
about _____ measure

2.
about _____ measure
about _____ measure

3.
about _____ measure
about _____ measure

12-1 Homework Practice
Nonstandard Units

Find the object. Estimate. Then use 🖇 to measure.

Answers will vary depending on size of classroom objects.

1. crayon

   Estimate: about _____ 🖇   Measure: about _____ 🖇

2. eraser

   Estimate: about _____ 🖇   Measure: about _____ 🖇

3. pencil

   Estimate: about _____ 🖇   Measure: about _____ 🖇

4. A ribbon is 30 🖇 long. Minny cuts off a piece of ribbon about 10 🖇 long. Write a number sentence to find how much ribbon is left.

   $30 - 10 = 20$ about **20** 🖇 left

12-1 Problem-Solving Practice
Nonstandard Units

Solve.

1. A pencil is about 7 🖇 long. A pen is about 9 🖇 long. About how much longer is the pen?

   $9 - 7 = 2$ 🖇

   The pen is about **2** longer.

2. A crayon is about 6 🖇 long. A paper clip is about 3 🖇 long. About how much shorter is the paper clip?

   $6 - 3 = 3$

   The paper clip is about **3** shorter.

3. Kat's red string is about 12 🖇 long. Her blue string is about 8 🖇 long. How do the lengths compare? The blue string is about **4** 🖇 shorter.

4. Fred's white straw is about 13 🖇 tall. His green straw is about 16 🖇 tall. About how much taller is Fred's green straw? The green straw is about **3** 🖇 taller.

5.

Paper Chain Contest	
Room	Length of Paper Chain
A	
B	
C	

   Which room has the longest paper chain? **C**

6. A fork is 8 🖇 long. A spoon is 6 🖇 long. A napkin is 9 🖇 long. Write three number sentences that compare the lengths of the napkin, fork, and spoon.

   $9 - 8 = 1$; $8 - 6 = 2$;
   $9 - 6 = 3$

Answers

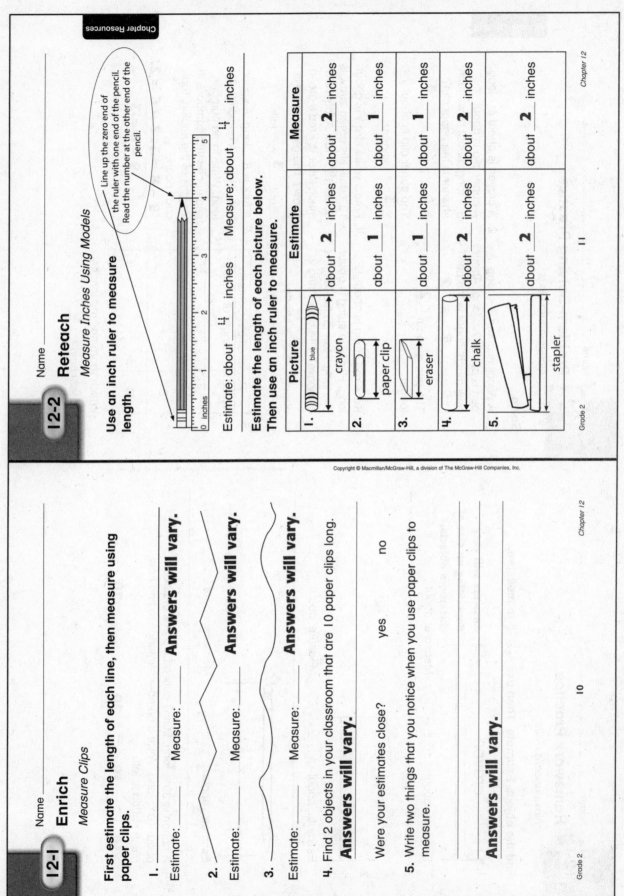

Chapter Resources

Name _____

Reteach 12-2

Measure Inches Using Models

Use an inch ruler to measure length.

Line up the zero end of the ruler with one end of the pencil. Read the number at the other end of the pencil.

0 inches   1   2   3   4   5

Estimate: about ___ inches   Measure: about ___ inches

Estimate the length of each picture below. Then use an inch ruler to measure.

Picture	Estimate	Measure
1. crayon	about **2** inches	about **2** inches
2. paper clip	about **1** inches	about **1** inches
3. eraser	about **1** inches	about **1** inches
4. chalk	about **2** inches	about **2** inches
5. stapler	about **2** inches	about **2** inches

Grade 2   11   Chapter 12

Name _____

Enrich 12-1

Measure Clips

First estimate the length of each line, then measure using paper clips.

1. Estimate: _____   Measure: _____ **Answers will vary.**

2. Estimate: _____   Measure: _____ **Answers will vary.**

3. Estimate: _____   Measure: _____ **Answers will vary.**

4. Find 2 objects in your classroom that are 10 paper clips long.

Answers will vary.

Were your estimates close?   yes   no

5. Write two things that you notice when you use paper clips to measure.

Answers will vary.

Grade 2   10   Chapter 12

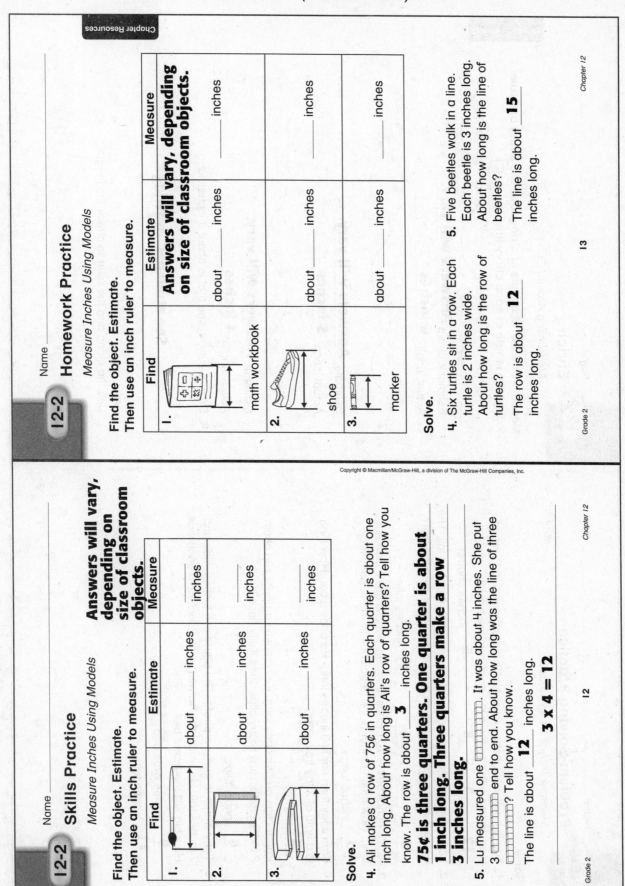

12-2 Skills Practice

Measure Inches Using Models

Find the object. Estimate.
Then use an inch ruler to measure.

Answers will vary, depending on size of classroom objects.

Find	Estimate	Measure
1.	about _____ inches	_____ inches
2.	about _____ inches	_____ inches
3.	about _____ inches	_____ inches

Solve.

4. Ali makes a row of 75¢ in quarters. Each quarter is about one inch long. About how long is Ali's row of quarters? Tell how you know. The row is about __3__ inches long.

75¢ is three quarters. One quarter is about 1 inch long. Three quarters make a row 3 inches long.

5. Lu measured one ▭▭▭. It was about 4 inches. She put ▭▭▭ ▭▭▭ end to end. About how long was the line of three ▭▭▭? Tell how you know.

The line is about __12__ inches long.

3 x 4 = 12

Grade 2   12   Chapter 12

Name _____

12-2 Homework Practice

Measure Inches Using Models

Find the object. Estimate.
Then use an inch ruler to measure.

Answers will vary, depending on size of classroom objects.

Find	Estimate	Measure
1. math workbook	about _____ inches	_____ inches
2. shoe	about _____ inches	_____ inches
3. marker	about _____ inches	_____ inches

Solve.

4. Six turtles sit in a row. Each turtle is 2 inches wide. About how long is the row of turtles?

The row is about __12__ inches long.

5. Five beetles walk in a line. Each beetle is 3 inches long. About how long is the line of beetles?

The line is about __15__ inches long.

Grade 2   13   Chapter 12

Answers

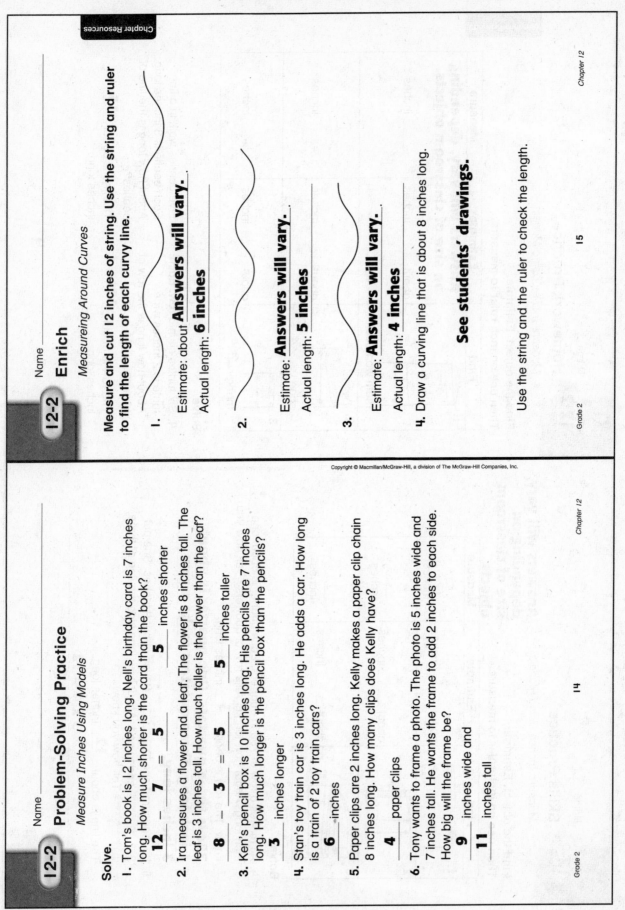

Name _____

12-2 Enrich

Measureing Around Curves

Measure and cut 12 inches of string. Use the string and ruler to find the length of each curvy line.

1.

Estimate: about **Answers will vary.**
Actual length: **6 inches**

2.

Estimate: **Answers will vary.**
Actual length: **5 inches**

3.

Estimate: **Answers will vary.**
Actual length: **4 inches**

4. Draw a curving line that is about 8 inches long.

See students' drawings.

Use the string and the ruler to check the length.

Name _____

12-2 Problem-Solving Practice

Measure Inches Using Models

Solve.

1. Tom's book is 12 inches long. Nell's birthday card is 7 inches long. How much shorter is the card than the book?

   12 – **7** = **5**   **5** inches shorter

2. Ira measures a flower and a leaf. The flower is 8 inches tall. The leaf is 3 inches tall. How much taller is the flower than the leaf?

   8 – **3** = **5**   **5** inches taller

3. Ken's pencil box is 10 inches long. His pencils are 7 inches long. How much longer is the pencil box than the pencils?

   3 inches longer

4. Stan's toy train car is 3 inches long. He adds a car. How long is a train of 2 toy train cars?

   6 inches

5. Paper clips are 2 inches long. Kelly makes a paper clip chain 8 inches long. How many clips does Kelly have?

   4 paper clips

6. Tony wants to frame a photo. The photo is 5 inches wide and 7 inches tall. He wants the frame to add 2 inches to each side. How big will the frame be?

   9 inches wide and
   11 inches tall

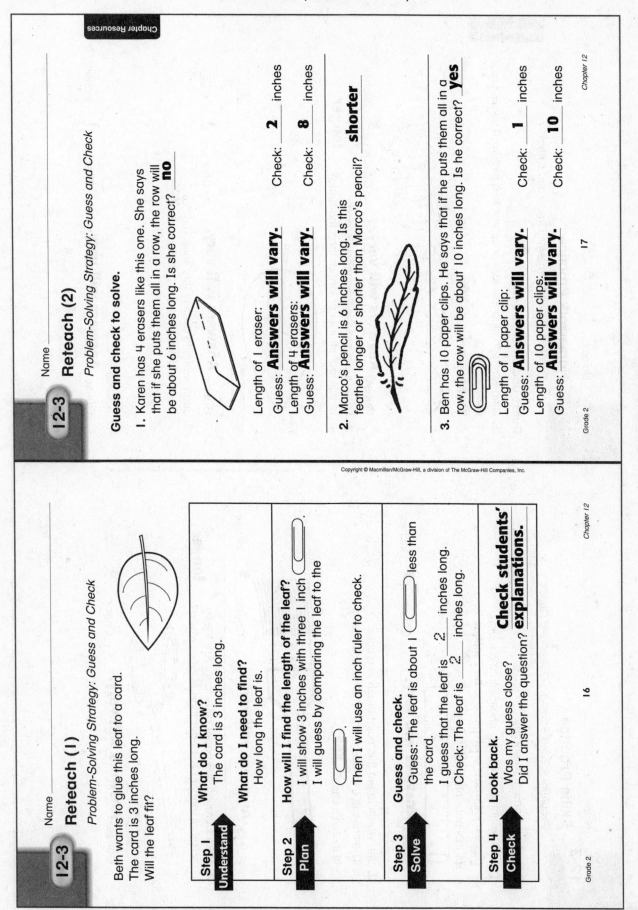

Name _____

12-3 Reteach (2)

Problem-Solving Strategy: Guess and Check

Guess and check to solve.

1. Karen has 4 erasers like this one. She says that if she puts them all in a row, the row will be about 6 inches long. Is she correct? __**no**__

Length of 1 eraser:
Guess: **Answers will vary.**   Check: __2__ inches

Length of 4 erasers:
Guess: **Answers will vary.**   Check: __8__ inches

2. Marco's pencil is 6 inches long. Is this feather longer or shorter than Marco's pencil? __**shorter**__

3. Ben has 10 paper clips. He says that if he puts them all in a row, the row will be about 10 inches long. Is he correct? __**yes**__

Length of 1 paper clip:
Guess: **Answers will vary.**   Check: __1__ inches

Length of 10 paper clips:
Guess: **Answers will vary.**   Check: __10__ inches

Name _____

12-3 Reteach (1)

Problem-Solving Strategy: Guess and Check

Beth wants to glue this leaf to a card.
The card is 3 inches long.
Will the leaf fit?

Step 1 Understand

What do I know?
The card is 3 inches long.

What do I need to find?
How long the leaf is.

Step 2 Plan

How will I find the length of the leaf?
I will show 3 inches with three 1 inch ____.
I will guess by comparing the leaf to the ____.
Then I will use an inch ruler to check.

Step 3 Solve

Guess and check.
Guess: The leaf is about 1 ____ less than the card.
I guess that the leaf is __2__ inches long.
Check: The leaf is __2__ inches long.

Step 4 Check

Look back.
Was my guess close?
Did I answer the question? **Check students' explanations.**

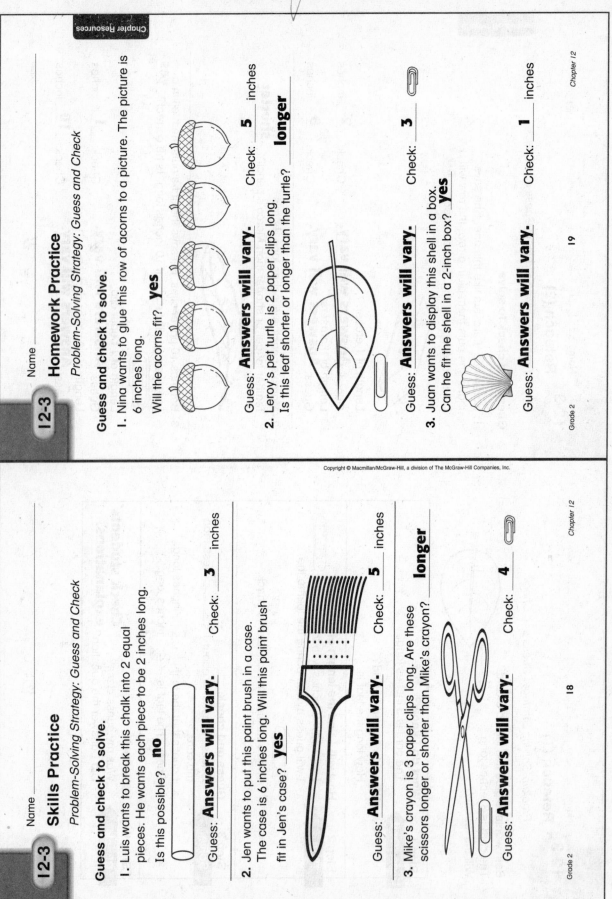

12-3 Homework Practice

Name _____

Problem-Solving Strategy: Guess and Check

Guess and check to solve.

1. Nina wants to glue this row of acorns to a picture. The picture is 6 inches long.
Will the acorns fit? __yes__

Guess: **Answers will vary.**   Check: __5__ inches

2. Leroy's pet turtle is 2 paper clips long. Is this leaf shorter or longer than the turtle? __longer__

Guess: **Answers will vary.**   Check: __3__

3. Juan wants to display this shell in a box. Can he fit the shell in a 2-inch box? __yes__

Guess: **Answers will vary.**   Check: __1__ inches

Grade 2   19   Chapter 12

12-3 Skills Practice

Name _____

Problem-Solving Strategy: Guess and Check

Guess and check to solve.

1. Luis wants to break this chalk into 2 equal pieces. He wants each piece to be 2 inches long.
Is this possible? __no__

Guess: **Answers will vary.**   Check: __3__ inches

2. Jen wants to put this paint brush in a case. The case is 6 inches long. Will this paint brush fit in Jen's case? __yes__

Guess: **Answers will vary.**   Check: __5__ inches

3. Mike's crayon is 3 paper clips long. Are these scissors longer or shorter than Mike's crayon? __longer__

Guess: **Answers will vary.**   Check: __4__

Grade 2   18   Chapter 12

Answers (Lessons 12-3 and 12-4)

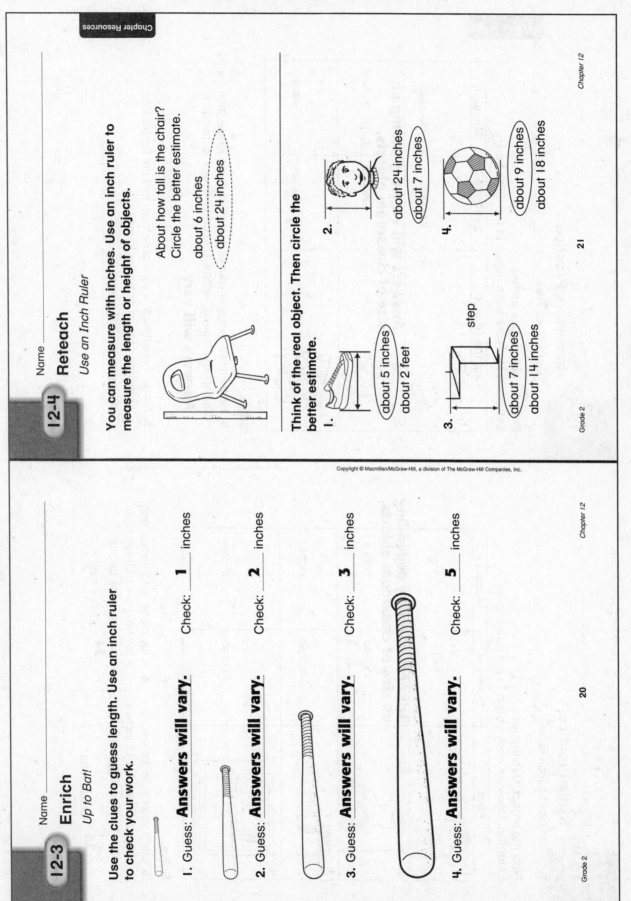

12-4

Name

Reteach

Use an Inch Ruler

You can measure with inches. Use an inch ruler to measure the length or height of objects.

About how tall is the chair?
Circle the better estimate.

about 6 inches

(about 24 inches)

Think of the real object. Then circle the better estimate.

1.
about 5 inches
about 2 feet

2.
about 24 inches
(about 7 inches)

3. step
(about 7 inches)
about 14 inches

4.
(about 9 inches)
about 18 inches

Grade 2
21
Chapter 12

12-3

Name

Enrich

Up to Bat!

Use the clues to guess length. Use an inch ruler to check your work.

1. Guess: **Answers will vary.**   Check: **1** _____ inches

2. Guess: **Answers will vary.**   Check: **2** _____ inches

3. Guess: **Answers will vary.**   Check: **3** _____ inches

4. Guess: **Answers will vary.**   Check: **5** _____ inches

Grade 2
20
Chapter 12

Answers (Lesson 12-4)

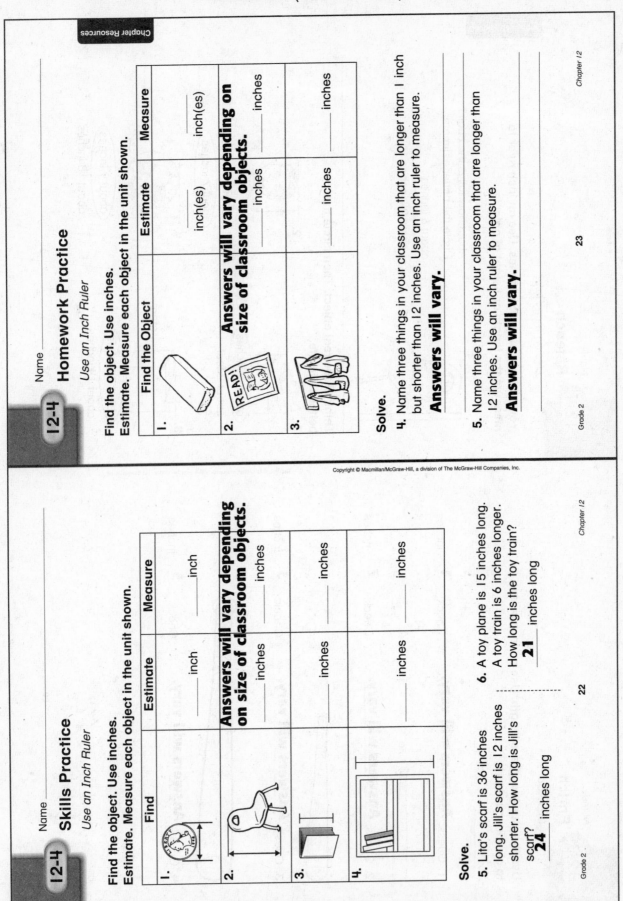

Homework Practice

Name _____

12-4

Use an Inch Ruler

Find the object. Use inches.
Estimate. Measure each object in the unit shown.

Find the Object	Estimate	Measure
1.	_____ inch(es)	_____ inch(es)
2.	**Answers will vary depending on size of classroom objects.**	
3.	_____ inches	_____ inches
	_____ inches	_____ inches

Solve.

4. Name three things in your classroom that are longer than 1 inch but shorter than 12 inches. Use an inch ruler to measure.
   Answers will vary.

5. Name three things in your classroom that are longer than 12 inches. Use an inch ruler to measure.
   Answers will vary.

Grade 2   23   *Chapter 12*

Skills Practice

Name _____

12-4

Use an Inch Ruler

Find the object. Use inches.
Estimate. Measure each object in the unit shown.

Find	Estimate	Measure
1.	_____ inch	_____ inch
2.	**Answers will vary depending on size of classroom objects.**	
3.	_____ inches	_____ inches
4.	_____ inches	_____ inches
	_____ inches	_____ inches

Solve.

5. Lita's scarf is 36 inches long. Jill's scarf is 12 inches shorter. How long is Jill's scarf?
   24 _____ inches long

6. A toy plane is 15 inches long. A toy train is 6 inches longer. How long is the toy train?
   21 _____ inches long

Grade 2   22   *Chapter 12*

12-4

Name _____

Problem-Solving Practice

Use an Inch Ruler

Solve.

| 1 foot = 12 inches |
| 1 yard = 3 feet |

1. Ann's dad gave her a 24-inch doll and a 36-inch bat. How much longer is the bat?

   12 inches

2. Nate's baby snake is 7 inches long. It grows to 36 inches. How much did the snake grow?

   29 inches

3. Mr. Ryan's class planted a 9-inch tall tree. It is now 48 inches tall. How many inches did it grow?

   39 inches

4. Rosa's poster is 12 inches long. Pat's poster is 14 inches long. How long are their posters together?

   26 inches

5. Jake draws a line that is 72 inches long. Ted draws a line that is 8 inches longer. How long is Ted's line?

   80 inches

6. Ms. Li's class has a fish tank that is 42 inches long. Mr. Kent's class tank is 30 inches long. How much longer is Ms. Li's class tank?

   12 inches

12-4

Name _____

Enrich

Use an Inch Ruler

Play this game with a partner. Cut out the cards at the bottom of the page to play.

How to Play

- A player picks one card and estimates the object.
- The other player uses a ruler to find the actual measurement.
- If the estimate is close to the actual measurement, the first player gets a point.
- Continue taking turns until a player gets 10 points.

a book	chair leg	paper clip	table leg
supply box	stapler	chalk	eraser
a shoe	crayon	pencil	door

Answers

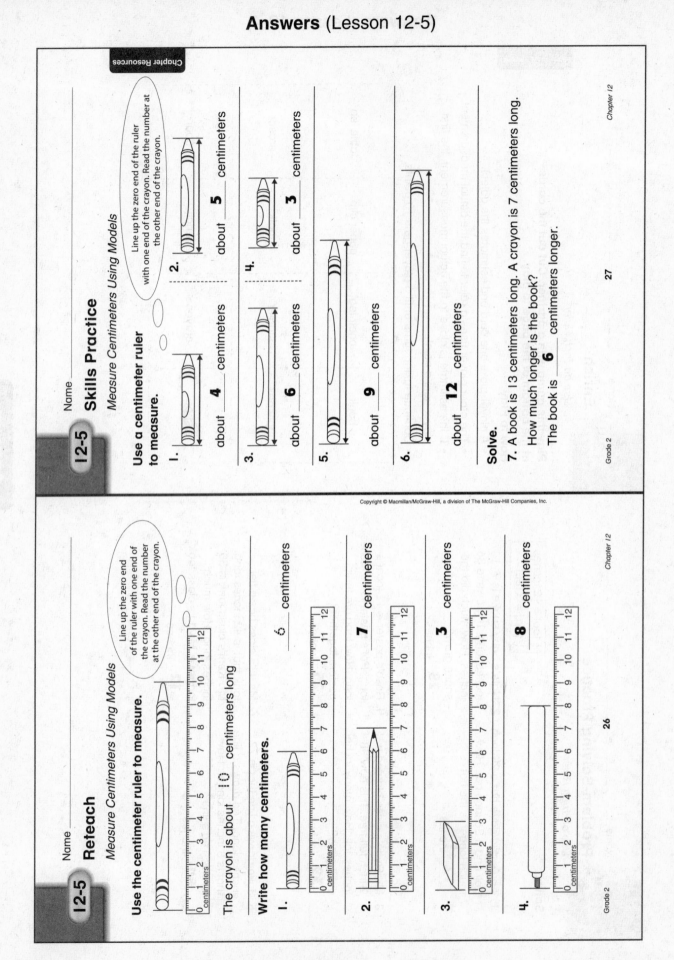

12-5

Name _____

Skills Practice
Measure Centimeters Using Models

Line up the zero end of the ruler with one end of the crayon. Read the number at the other end of the crayon.

Use a centimeter ruler to measure.

1. about **4** centimeters

2. about **5** centimeters

3. about **6** centimeters

4. about **3** centimeters

5. about **9** centimeters

6. about **12** centimeters

Solve.

7. A book is 13 centimeters long. A crayon is 7 centimeters long. How much longer is the book?

The book is **6** centimeters longer.

Grade 2   27   Chapter 12

12-5

Name _____

Reteach
Measure Centimeters Using Models

Line up the zero end of the ruler with one end of the crayon. Read the number at the other end of the crayon.

Use the centimeter ruler to measure.

The crayon is about **10** centimeters long

Write how many centimeters.

1. **6** centimeters

2. **7** centimeters

3. **3** centimeters

4. **8** centimeters

Grade 2   26   Chapter 12

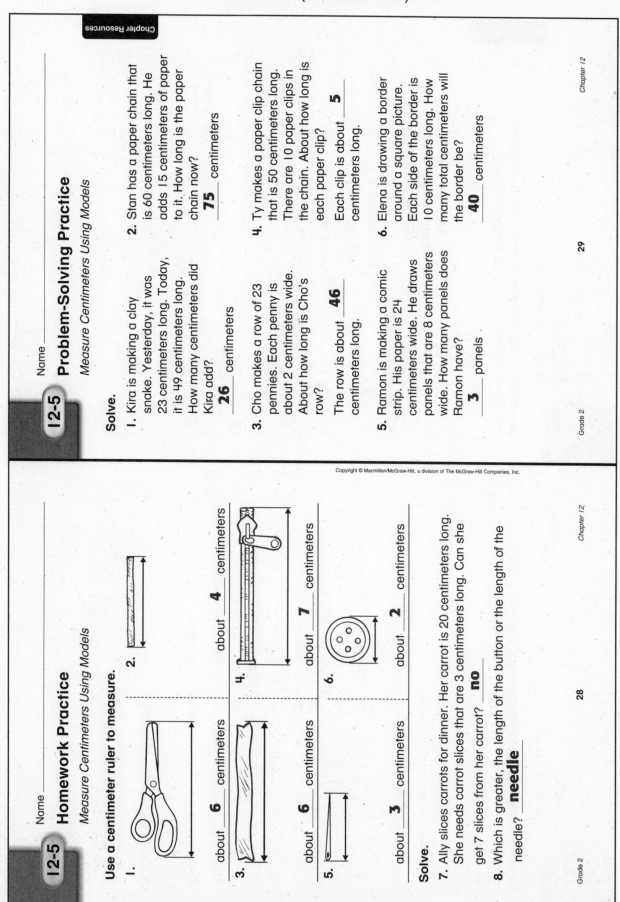

Problem-Solving Practice

Measure Centimeters Using Models

Name _____

12-5

Solve.

1. Kira is making a clay snake. Yesterday, it was 23 centimeters long. Today, it is 49 centimeters long. How many centimeters did Kira add?

26 centimeters

2. Stan has a paper chain that is 60 centimeters long. He adds 15 centimeters of paper to it. How long is the paper chain now?

75 centimeters

3. Cho makes a row of 23 pennies. Each penny is about 2 centimeters wide. About how long is Cho's row?

The row is about **46** centimeters long.

4. Ty makes a paper clip chain that is 50 centimeters long. There are 10 paper clips in the chain. About how long is each paper clip?

Each clip is about **5** centimeters long.

5. Ramon is making a comic strip. His paper is 24 centimeters wide. He draws panels that are 8 centimeters wide. How many panels does Ramon have?

3 panels

6. Elena is drawing a border around a square picture. Each side of the border is 10 centimeters long. How many total centimeters will the border be?

40 centimeters

Grade 2   29   Chapter 12

Homework Practice

Measure Centimeters Using Models

Name _____

12-5

Use a centimeter ruler to measure.

1.

2.

3.

about **6** centimeters

about **6** centimeters

about **4** centimeters

4.

about **7** centimeters

5.

about **3** centimeters

6.

about **2** centimeters

Solve.

7. Ally slices carrots for dinner. Her carrot is 20 centimeters long. She needs carrot slices that are 3 centimeters long. Can she get 7 slices from her carrot? **no**

8. Which is greater, the length of the button or the length of the needle? **needle**

Grade 2   28   Chapter 12

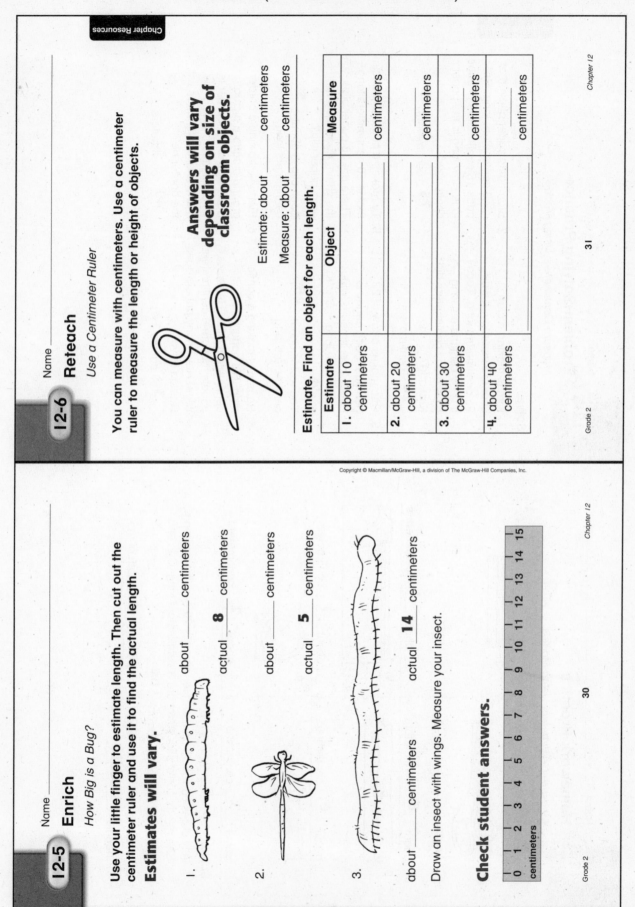

Name _____

12-6 Reteach

Use a Centimeter Ruler

You can measure with centimeters. Use a centimeter ruler to measure the length or height of objects.

Answers will vary depending on size of classroom objects.

Estimate: about _____ centimeters

Measure: about _____ centimeters

Estimate. Find an object for each length.

Estimate	Object	Measure
1. about 10 centimeters		_____ centimeters
2. about 20 centimeters		_____ centimeters
3. about 30 centimeters		_____ centimeters
4. about 40 centimeters		_____ centimeters

Name _____

12-5 Enrich

How Big is a Bug?

Use your little finger to estimate length. Then cut out the centimeter ruler and use it to find the actual length.

Estimates will vary.

1. about _____ centimeters

   actual **8** centimeters

2. about _____ centimeters

   actual **5** centimeters

3. about _____ centimeters

   actual **14** centimeters

about _____ centimeters

Draw an insect with wings. Measure your insect.

Check student answers.

centimeters
0 1 2 3 4 5 6 7 8 9 10 11 12 13 14 15

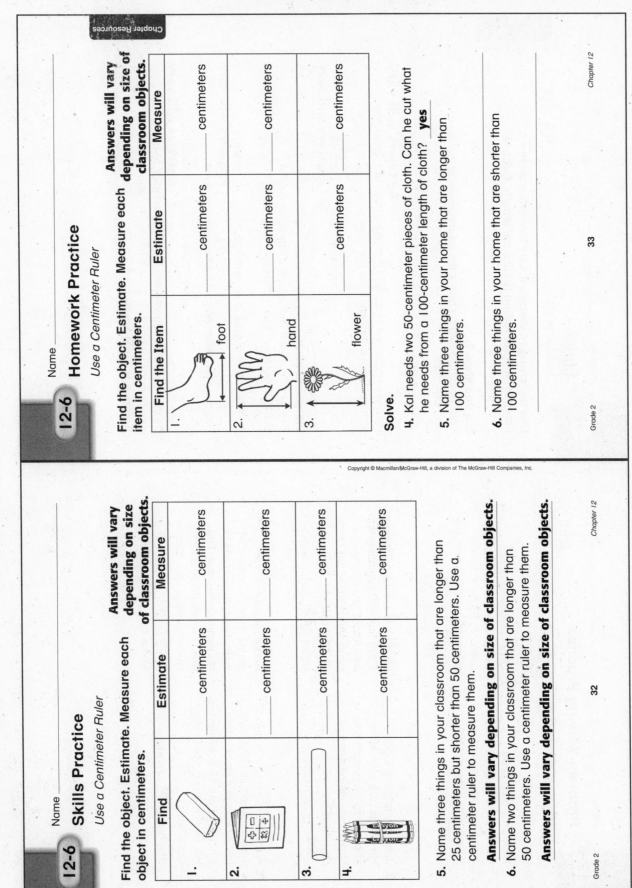

Chapter Resources

12-6

Homework Practice

Use a Centimeter Ruler

Find the object. Estimate. Measure each item in centimeters.

Answers will vary depending on size of classroom objects.

Find the Item	Estimate	Measure
1. foot	_____ centimeters	_____ centimeters
2. hand	_____ centimeters	_____ centimeters
3. flower	_____ centimeters	_____ centimeters

Solve.

4. Kal needs two 50-centimeter pieces of cloth. Can he cut what he needs from a 100-centimeter length of cloth? **yes**

5. Name three things in your home that are longer than 100 centimeters.

6. Name three things in your home that are shorter than 100 centimeters.

Grade 2   33   Chapter 12

12-6

Skills Practice

Use a Centimeter Ruler

Find the object. Estimate. Measure each object in centimeters.

Answers will vary depending on size of classroom objects.

Find	Estimate	Measure
1.	_____ centimeters	_____ centimeters
2.	_____ centimeters	_____ centimeters
3.	_____ centimeters	_____ centimeters
4.	_____ centimeters	_____ centimeters

5. Name three things in your classroom that are longer than 25 centimeters but shorter than 50 centimeters. Use a centimeter ruler to measure them.

Answers will vary depending on size of classroom objects.

6. Name two things in your classroom that are longer than 50 centimeters. Use a centimeter ruler to measure them.

Answers will vary depending on size of classroom objects.

Grade 2   32   Chapter 12

Answers

12-6 Enrich

Name _____

Measuring Me

Use the string to measure. Lay the string on the centimeter ruler to find the actual length. Record your answers.

Did you know?
Your height should be about the same distance as your arm span.

1. Your height: _____ estimate _____ actual _____ **Answers will vary.**

Hold your arms out like a bird. Measure your arm span, the distance from one fingertip to the other:

_____ estimate _____ actual _____ **Answers will vary.**

Did you know?
The length of your foot is about the same as the distance between your elbow and your wrist.

2. The length of your foot: estimate _____ actual _____ **Answers will vary.**

The distance between your elbow and your wrist:

estimate _____ actual _____ **Answers will vary.**

Do you think that centimeters are a good choice to use when measuring your height? Give a reason for your answer.
Answers will vary.

12-6 Problem-Solving Practice

Name _____

Use a Centimeter Ruler

Solve.

1. Rick's toy train is 89 centimeters long. Ali's toy train is 98 centimeter long. Who has the longer toy?
   Ali

2. Lin's fish poster is 125 centimeters tall. Her cow poster is 55 centimeters shorter. How tall is her cow poster?
   70 centimeters

3. Jose is wrapping 3 gifts. He needs 30 centimeters of paper to wrap each one. How many centimeters of paper will he use?
   90 centimeters

4. Mr. Kim is stacking 7 boxes. Each box is 5 centimeters tall. About how many centimeters tall is the stack of 7 boxes?
   about **35** centimeters

5. A stack of 5 nickels is about 1 centimeter tall. Cass puts her nickels in a stack. Her stack is about 16 centimeters tall. How many nickels does Cass have?
   She has **80** nickels.

6. Andre measures one penny. It is 2 centimeters wide. Next, Andre puts all his pennies in a row. The row is 64 centimeters long. How many pennies does Andre have?
   Andre has **32** pennies.

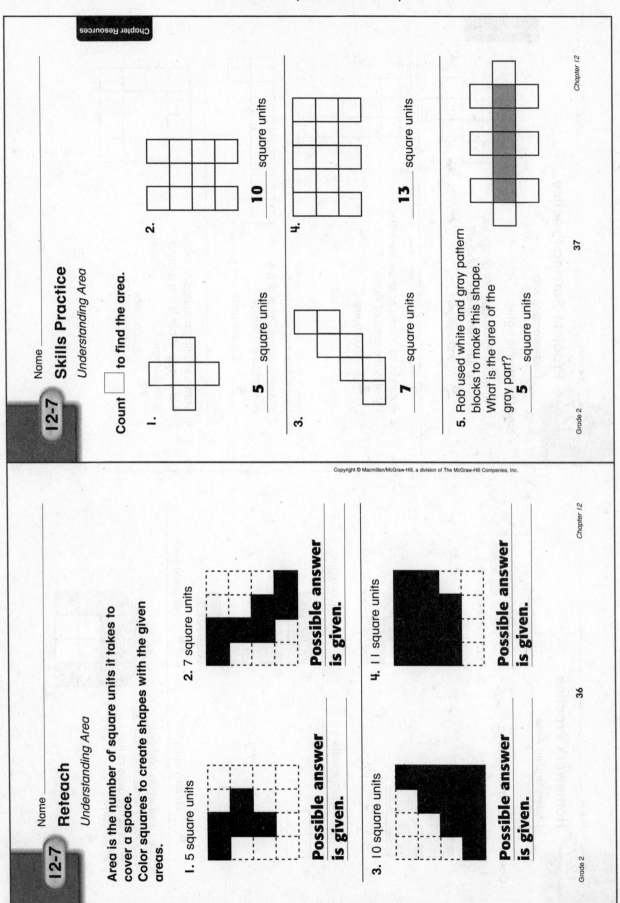

Chapter Resources

Name _____

Skills Practice
Understanding Area

12-7

Count ⬜ to find the area.

1.

2.

10 square units

3.

5 square units

4.

13 square units

7 square units

5. Rob used white and gray pattern blocks to make this shape. What is the area of the gray part?

5 square units

Name _____

Reteach
Understanding Area

12-7

Area is the number of square units it takes to cover a space.
Color squares to create shapes with the given areas.

1. 5 square units

Possible answer is given.

2. 7 square units

Possible answer is given.

3. 10 square units

Possible answer is given.

4. 11 square units

Possible answer is given.

Answers

Answers (Lesson 12-7)

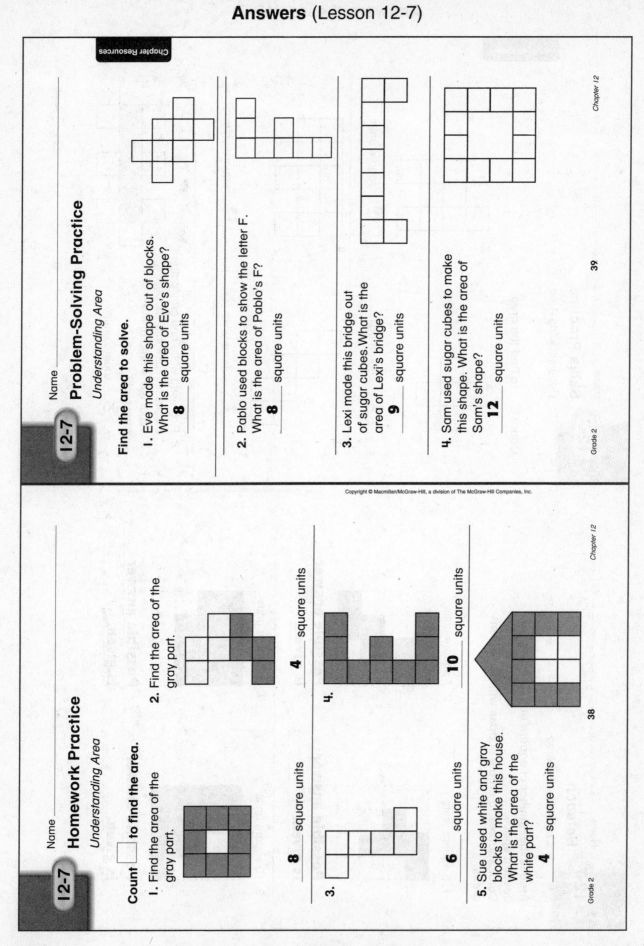

12-7 Problem-Solving Practice

Understanding Area

Find the area to solve.

1. Eve made this shape out of blocks. What is the area of Eve's shape?

   8 _____ square units

2. Pablo used blocks to show the letter F. What is the area of Pablo's F?

   8 _____ square units

3. Lexi made this bridge out of sugar cubes. What is the area of Lexi's bridge?

   9 _____ square units

4. Sam used sugar cubes to make this shape. What is the area of Sam's shape?

   12 _____ square units

12-7 Homework Practice

Understanding Area

Count ▢ **to find the area.**

1. Find the area of the gray part.

2. Find the area of the gray part.

   _____ **4** square units

   8 _____ square units

3. _____ **6** square units

4. _____ **10** square units

5. Sue used white and gray blocks to make this house. What is the area of the white part?

   _____ **4** square units

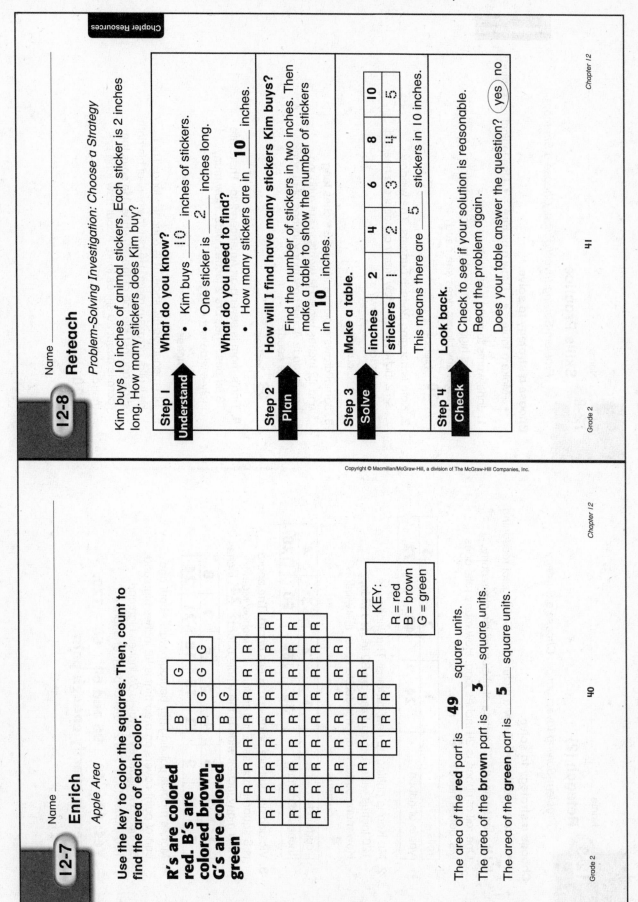

12-8

Name _____

Reteach
Problem-Solving Investigation: Choose a Strategy

Kim buys 10 inches of animal stickers. Each sticker is 2 inches long. How many stickers does Kim buy?

Step 1 — Understand

What do you know?
- Kim buys __10__ inches of stickers.
- One sticker is __2__ inches long.

What do you need to find?
- How many stickers are in __10__ inches.

Step 2 — Plan

How will I find have many stickers Kim buys?

Find the number of stickers in two inches. Then make a table to show the number of stickers in __10__ inches.

Step 3 — Solve

Make a table.

inches	2	4	6	8	10
stickers	1	2	3	4	5

This means there are __5__ stickers in 10 inches.

Step 4 — Check

Look back.

Check to see if your solution is reasonable.

Read the problem again.

Does your table answer the question? (yes) no

Grade 2   41   *Chapter 12*

12-7

Name _____

Enrich
Apple Area

Use the key to color the squares. Then, count to find the area of each color.

R's are colored red. B's are colored brown. G's are colored green

		B	G	
R	R	B	G	G	G
R	R	B	G
R	R	R	R	R	R	R
R	R	R	R	R	R	R	R
R	R	R	R	R	R	R	R
R	R	R	R	R	R	R	R
R	R	R	R	R	R	R	R
	R	R	R	R

KEY:
R = red
B = brown
G = green

The area of the **red** part is __49__ square units.

The area of the **brown** part is __3__ square units.

The area of the **green** part is __5__ square units.

Grade 2   40   *Chapter 12*

Name _____

12-8 Skills Practice

Problem-Solving Investigation: Choose a Strategy

Choose a strategy to solve.

- Make a table
- Draw a picture
- Use logical reasoning

1. Jane wants to build a block tower that is 40 inches high. Each block is 2 inches high. How many blocks does she need?

   20 blocks

2. Koto is hanging 36-inch curtains. The window is 72 inches wide. How many curtains are needed to cover the window?

   2 curtains

3. Jamal draws a picture that is 22 inches long and 22 inches wide. He wants to put a ribbon border on it. About how many inches of ribbon does he need?

   88 inches

4. Tina's mom is sewing an American flag. There are 13 stripes. They are 2 inches wide. How many inches wide is the flag?

   26 inches

5. Tim measures his shoe. It is 6 inches long. Then, he walks across a room. He put the heel of his right shoe against the toe of the left shoe. He says the room is about 20 shoes long. About how long is the room in inches?

   120 inches

Grade 2   43   Chapter 12

Name _____

12-8 Reteach (2)

Problem-Solving Investigation: Choose a Strategy

Choose a strategy to solve.

- Make a table
- Draw a picture
- Use logical reasoning

1. Ms. Jones needs 72 inches of ribbon for the class party. One roll of ribbon is 24 inches long. How many rolls does Ms. Jones need? **3** rolls

rolls	1	2	3
yards of ribbon	24	48	72

2. Mr. Karr is putting up new curtains. The window is 120 inches wide. His curtains are 30 inches wide. How many curtains are needed to cover the window? **4** curtains

curtains	1	2	3	4
inches of curtain	30	60	90	120

3. Vic and his dad are painting a chess board. The board is 8 squares across. Each square is 3 inches across. How many inches wide is the whole board? **24** inches

1	2	3	4	5	6	7	8
3	6	9	12	15	18	21	24

4. Mary's mom is painting her bedroom wall. About one can of paint covers an area that is 48 inches high and 60 inches long. Mary's wall is 96 inches high and 120 inches long. Are 2 cans of paint enough?

   Yes; 48 + 48 = 96 and 60 + 60 = 120. There is exactly enough paint.

Grade 2   42   Chapter 12

Grade 2   A20   Chapter 12

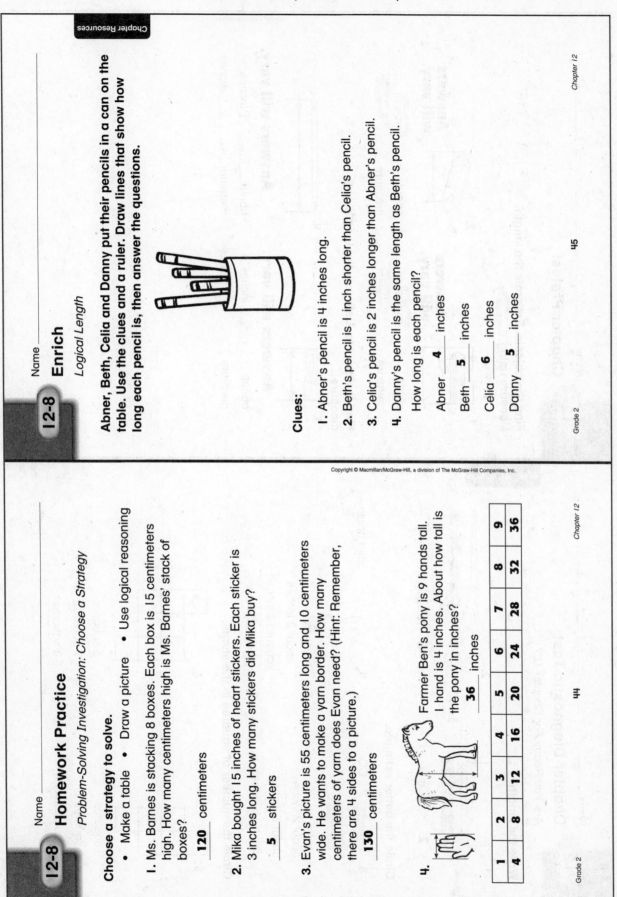

Name _____

12-8 Enrich

Logical Length

Abner, Beth, Celia and Danny put their pencils in a can on the table. Use the clues and a ruler. Draw lines that show how long each pencil is, then answer the questions.

Clues:

1. Abner's pencil is 4 inches long.

2. Beth's pencil is 1 inch shorter than Celia's pencil.

3. Celia's pencil is 2 inches longer than Abner's pencil.

4. Danny's pencil is the same length as Beth's pencil.

How long is each pencil?

Abner ___**4**___ inches

Beth ___**5**___ inches

Celia ___**6**___ inches

Danny ___**5**___ inches

Grade 2   45   *Chapter 12*

Name _____

12-8 Homework Practice

Problem-Solving Investigation: Choose a Strategy

Choose a strategy to solve.

- Make a table
- Draw a picture
- Use logical reasoning

1. Ms. Barnes is stacking 8 boxes. Each box is 15 centimeters high. How many centimeters high is Ms. Barnes' stack of boxes?

   ___**120**___ centimeters

2. Mika bought 15 inches of heart stickers. Each sticker is 3 inches long. How many stickers did Mika buy?

   ___**5**___ stickers

3. Evan's picture is 55 centimeters long and 10 centimeters wide. He wants to make a yarn border. How many centimeters of yarn does Evan need? (Hint: Remember, there are 4 sides to a picture.)

   ___**130**___ centimeters

4. Farmer Ben's pony is 9 hands tall. 1 hand is 4 inches. About how tall is the pony in inches?

   ___**36**___ inches

1	2	3	4	5	6	7	8	9
4	8	12	16	20	24	28	32	36

Grade 2   44   *Chapter 12*

Answers

Answers (Chapter Diagnostic Test, Chapter Pretest)

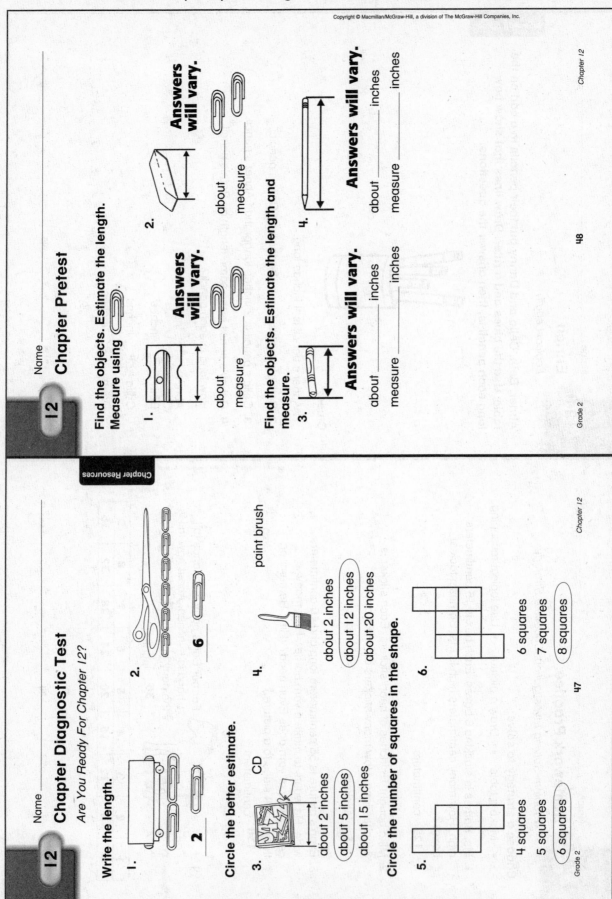

12 Chapter Pretest

Name _____

Find the objects. Estimate the length. Measure using 📎.

1.

about _____ **Answers will vary.**

measure _____

2.

about _____ **Answers will vary.**

measure _____

Find the objects. Estimate the length and measure.

3.

about _____ inches

measure _____ inches

Answers will vary.

4.

about _____ inches

measure _____ inches

Answers will vary.

Grade 2
48
Chapter 12

---

12 Chapter Diagnostic Test
Are You Ready For Chapter 12?

Name _____

Write the length.

1.

2

2.

6

Circle the better estimate.

3. CD

about 2 inches
(about 5 inches)
about 15 inches

4. paint brush

about 2 inches
(about 12 inches)
about 20 inches

Circle the number of squares in the shape.

5.

4 squares
5 squares
(6 squares)

6.

6 squares
7 squares
(8 squares)

Grade 2
47
Chapter 12

Chapter Resources

Answers (Mid-Chapter Test, Vocabulary Test)

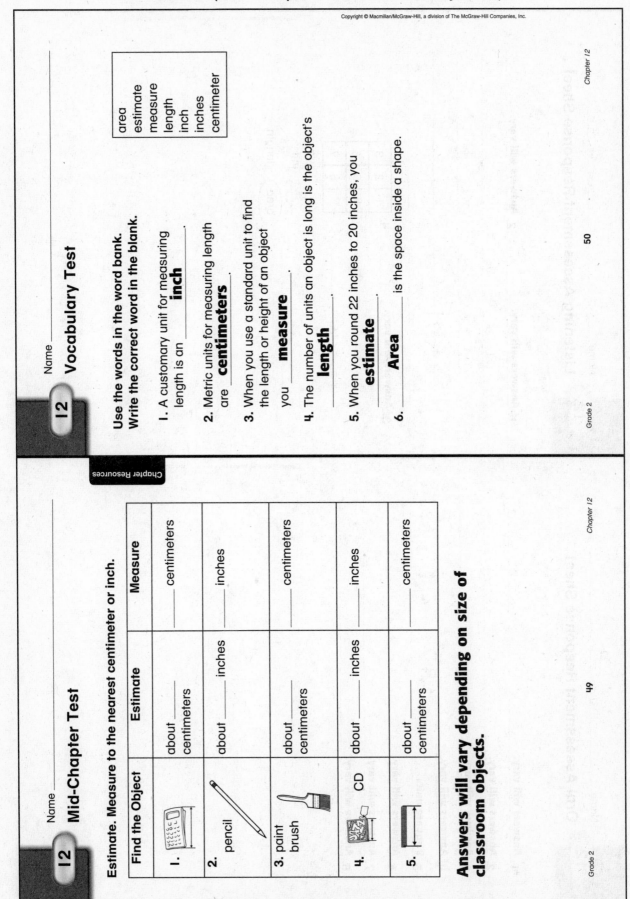

Vocabulary Test

12

Name _____

Use the words in the word bank.
Write the correct word in the blank.

word bank:
- area
- estimate
- measure
- length
- inch
- inches
- centimeter

1. A customary unit for measuring length is an __**inch**__.

2. Metric units for measuring length are __**centimeters**__.

3. When you use a standard unit to find the length or height of an object you __**measure**__.

4. The number of units an object is long is the object's __**length**__.

5. When you round 22 inches to 20 inches, you __**estimate**__.

6. __**Area**__ is the space inside a shape.

Mid-Chapter Test

12

Name _____

Estimate. Measure to the nearest centimeter or inch.

Find the Object	Estimate	Measure
1. calculator	about ____ centimeters	____ centimeters
2. pencil	about ____ inches	____ inches
3. paint brush	about ____ centimeters	____ centimeters
4. CD	about ____ inches	____ inches
5.	about ____ centimeters	____ centimeters

Answers will vary depending on size of classroom objects.

Answers (Oral & Listening Assessment Response Sheets)

12

Name _____

Listening Assessment Response Sheet

1. Answers will vary.

2. Answers will vary.

3. Answers will vary.

4.

1	2	3
4	5	6
7	8	9

9 ___ units

(area) ___ length

12

Name _____

Oral Assessment Response Sheet

1. Answers will vary.
2. Answers will vary.
3. Answers will vary.
4. Answers will vary.
5. 9 square units
6. Answers will vary.
7. Answers will vary.
8. Answers will vary.

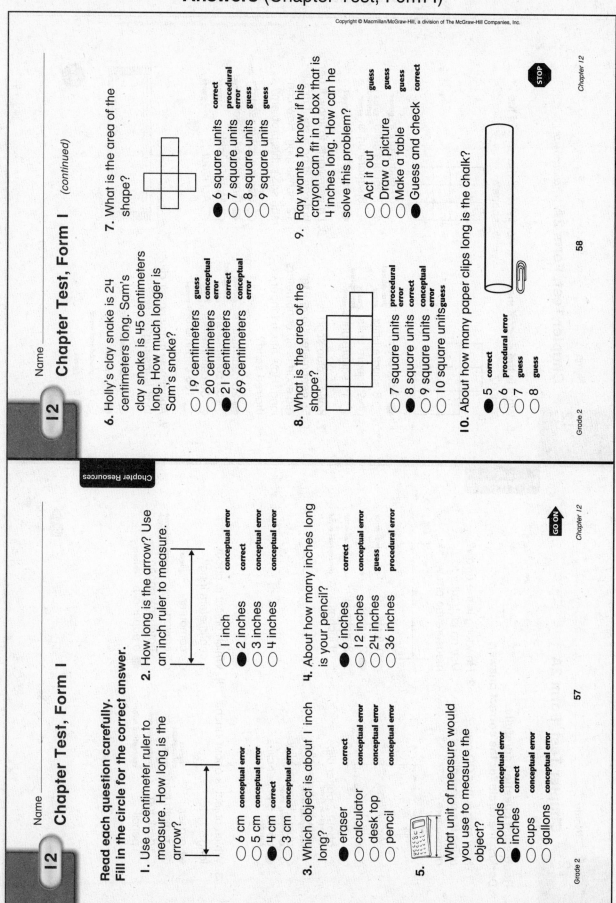

Name _____

12 Chapter Test, Form I

Read each question carefully.
Fill in the circle for the correct answer.

1. Use a centimeter ruler to measure. How long is the arrow?

- ○ 6 cm   conceptual error
- ○ 5 cm   conceptual error
- ● 4 cm   correct
- ○ 3 cm   conceptual error

2. How long is the arrow? Use an inch ruler to measure.

- ○ 1 inch   conceptual error
- ● 2 inches   correct
- ○ 3 inches   conceptual error
- ○ 4 inches   conceptual error

3. Which object is about 1 inch long?

- ● eraser   correct
- ○ calculator   conceptual error
- ○ desk top   conceptual error
- ○ pencil   conceptual error

4. About how many inches long is your pencil?

- ● 6 inches   correct
- ○ 12 inches   conceptual error
- ○ 24 inches   guess
- ○ 36 inches   procedural error

5. What unit of measure would you use to measure the object?

- ○ pounds   conceptual error
- ● inches   correct
- ○ cups   conceptual error
- ○ gallons   conceptual error

Name _____

12 Chapter Test, Form I   *(continued)*

6. Holly's clay snake is 24 centimeters long. Sam's clay snake is 45 centimeters long. How much longer is Sam's snake?

- ○ 19 centimeters   guess
- ○ 20 centimeters   conceptual error
- ● 21 centimeters   correct
- ○ 69 centimeters   conceptual error

7. What is the area of the shape?

- ● 6 square units   correct
- ○ 7 square units   procedural error
- ○ 8 square units   guess
- ○ 9 square units   guess

8. What is the area of the shape?

- ○ 7 square units   procedural error
- ● 8 square units   correct
- ○ 9 square units   conceptual error
- ○ 10 square units   guess

9. Ray wants to know if his crayon can fit in a box that is 4 inches long. How can he solve this problem?

- ○ Act it out   guess
- ○ Draw a picture   guess
- ○ Make a table   guess
- ● Guess and check   correct

10. About how many paper clips long is the chalk?

- ● 5   correct
- ○ 6   procedural error
- ○ 7   guess
- ○ 8   guess

STOP

Answers

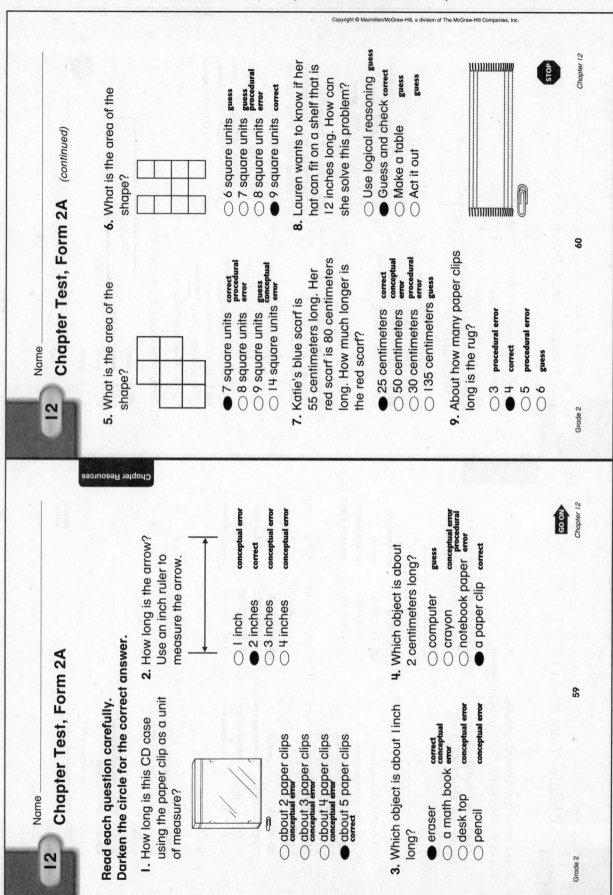

12

Name _____

Chapter Test, Form 2A

**Read each question carefully.
Darken the circle for the correct answer.**

1. How long is this CD case using the paper clip as a unit of measure?

- ○ about 2 paper clips — conceptual error
- ○ about 3 paper clips — conceptual error
- ○ about 4 paper clips — conceptual error
- ● about 5 paper clips — correct

2. How long is the arrow? Use an inch ruler to measure the arrow.

- ○ 1 inch — conceptual error
- ● 2 inches — correct
- ○ 3 inches — conceptual error
- ○ 4 inches — conceptual error

3. Which object is about 1 inch long?

- ● eraser — correct
- ○ a math book — conceptual error
- ○ desk top — conceptual error
- ○ pencil — conceptual error

4. Which object is about 2 centimeters long?

- ○ computer — guess
- ○ crayon — conceptual error
- ○ notebook paper — procedural error
- ● a paper clip — correct

Grade 2   59   Chapter 12 GO ON

Name _____

Chapter Test, Form 2A *(continued)*

5. What is the area of the shape?

- ● 7 square units — correct
- ○ 8 square units — procedural error
- ○ 9 square units — guess
- ○ 14 square units — conceptual error

6. What is the area of the shape?

- ○ 6 square units — guess
- ○ 7 square units — guess
- ○ 8 square units — procedural error
- ● 9 square units — correct

7. Katie's blue scarf is 55 centimeters long. Her red scarf is 80 centimeters long. How much longer is the red scarf?

- ● 25 centimeters — correct
- ○ 50 centimeters — conceptual error
- ○ 30 centimeters — procedural error
- ○ 135 centimeters — guess

8. Lauren wants to know if her hat can fit on a shelf that is 12 inches long. How can she solve this problem?

- ○ Use logical reasoning — guess
- ● Guess and check — correct
- ○ Make a table — guess
- ○ Act it out — guess

9. About how many paper clips long is the rug?

- ○ 3 — procedural error
- ● 4 — correct
- ○ 5 — procedural error
- ○ 6 — guess

Grade 2   60   Chapter 12 STOP

Chapter Resources

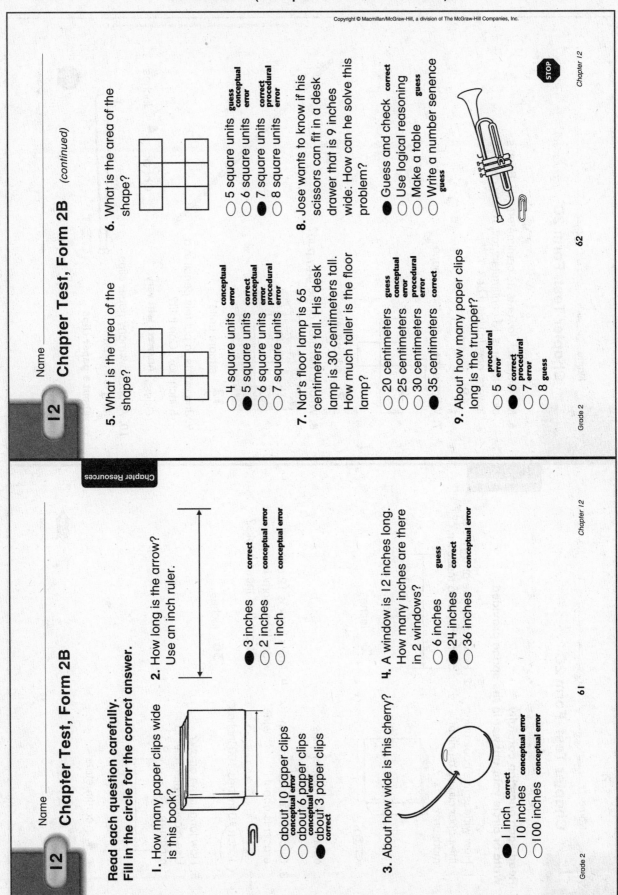

Name _____

12 **Chapter Test, Form 2B** *(continued)*

5. What is the area of the shape?

○ 4 square units   conceptual error
● 5 square units   correct
○ 6 square units   conceptual error
○ 7 square units   procedural error

6. What is the area of the shape?

○ 5 square units   guess
○ 6 square units   conceptual error
● 7 square units   correct
○ 8 square units   procedural error

7. Nat's floor lamp is 65 centimeters tall. His desk lamp is 30 centimeters tall. How much taller is the floor lamp?

○ 20 centimeters   guess
○ 25 centimeters   conceptual error
○ 30 centimeters   procedural error
● 35 centimeters   correct

8. Jose wants to know if his scissors can fit in a desk drawer that is 9 inches wide. How can he solve this problem?

● Guess and check   correct
○ Use logical reasoning
○ Make a table   guess
○ Write a number senence   guess

9. About how many paper clips long is the trumpet?

○ 5   procedural error
● 6   correct
○ 7   procedural error
○ 8   guess

Name _____

12 **Chapter Test, Form 2B**

Read each question carefully.
Fill in the circle for the correct answer.

1. How many paper clips wide is this book?

○ about 10 paper clips   conceptual error
○ about 6 paper clips   conceptual error
● about 3 paper clips   correct

2. How long is the arrow? Use an inch ruler.

● 3 inches   correct
○ 2 inches   conceptual error
○ 1 inch   conceptual error

3. About how wide is this cherry?

● 1 inch   correct
○ 10 inches   conceptual error
○ 100 inches   conceptual error

4. A window is 12 inches long. How many inches are there in 2 windows?

○ 6 inches   guess
● 24 inches   correct
○ 36 inches   conceptual error

Answers

Answers (Chapter Test, Form 2C)

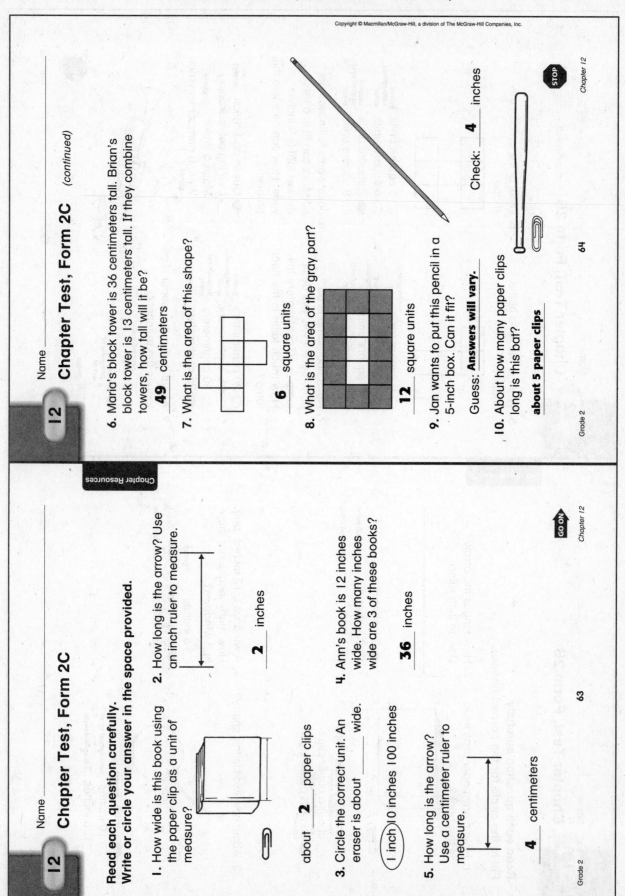

Name

12 Chapter Test, Form 2C

**Read each question carefully.
Write or circle your answer in the space provided.**

1. How wide is this book using the paper clip as a unit of measure?

about **2** paper clips

2. How long is the arrow? Use an inch ruler to measure.

2 inches

3. Circle the correct unit. An eraser is about ____ wide.

(1 inch) 10 inches 100 inches

4. Ann's book is 12 inches wide. How many inches wide are 3 of these books?

36 inches

5. How long is the arrow? Use a centimeter ruler to measure.

4 centimeters

Name

12 Chapter Test, Form 2C (continued)

6. Maria's block tower is 36 centimeters tall. Brian's block tower is 13 centimeters tall. If they combine towers, how tall will it be?

49 centimeters

7. What is the area of this shape?

6 square units

8. What is the area of the gray part?

12 square units

9. Jan wants to put this pencil in a 5-inch box. Can it fit?

Guess: **Answers will vary.**

Check: **4** inches

10. About how many paper clips long is this bat?

about 5 paper clips

Answers (Chapter Test, Form 2D)

Name _____

Chapter Test, Form 2D *(continued)*

12

6. Maria's block tower is 36 centimeters tall. Brian's block tower is 12 centimeters tall. How tall are they together?

48 centimeters

7. What is the area of this shape?

6 square units

8. What is the area of the gray part?

12 square units

9. Jan wants to put this pencil in a 5-inch box. Can it fit?

Guess: **Answers will vary.**

Check: **4** inches

yes

10. About how many paper clips long is this bat?

about 5 paper clips

Name _____

Chapter Test, Form 2D

12

Read each question carefully. Write or circle your answer in the space provided.

1. How many paper clips wide is this book?

about **2** paper clips

2. How long is the arrow? Use an inch ruler to measure.

2 inches

3. Circle the correct unit. How long is this sheet of paper?

about an inch
about 12 inches
about 24 inches

4. Ann's book is 10 inches wide. How wide are 3 books?

30 inches

5. How long is the arrow? Use a centimeter ruler to measure.

6 centimeters

Answers

Chapter Resources

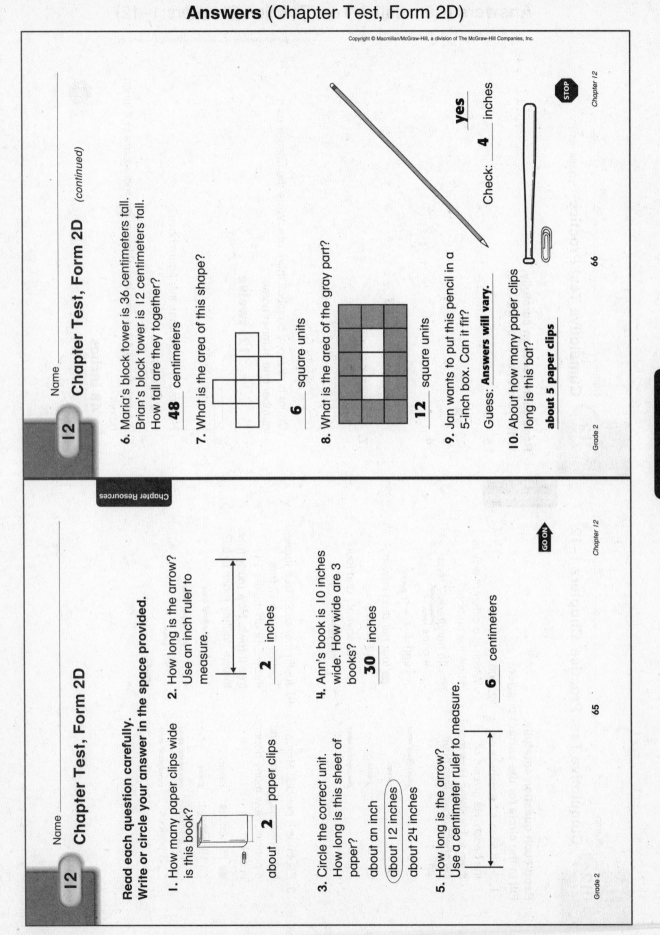

Answers (Cumulative Test Practice Chapters 1–12)

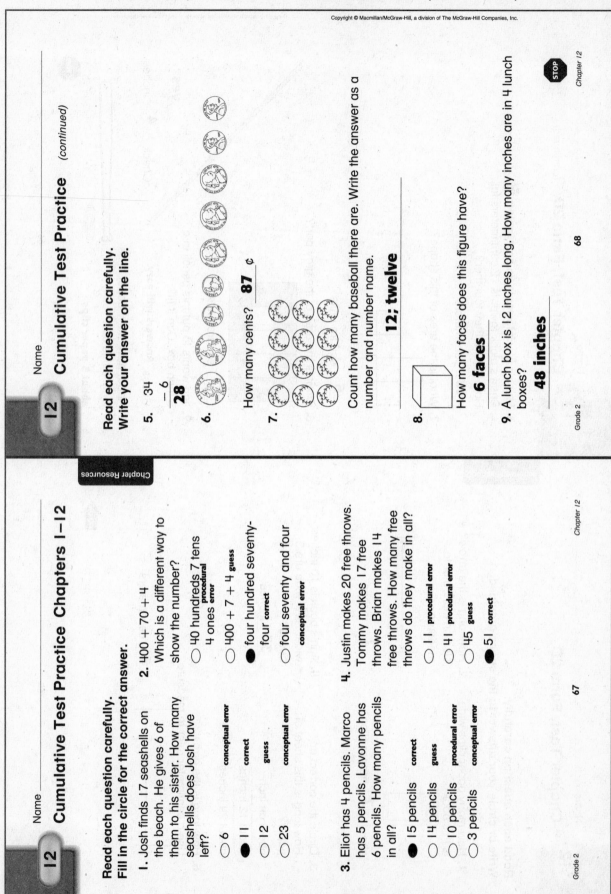

12

Name _____

Cumulative Test Practice Chapters 1–12

**Read each question carefully.
Fill in the circle for the correct answer.**

1. Josh finds 17 seashells on the beach. He gives 6 of them to his sister. How many seashells does Josh have left?

- ○ 6   **conceptual error**
- ● 11   **correct**
- ○ 12   **guess**
- ○ 23   **conceptual error**

2. $400 + 70 + 4$ Which is a different way to show the number?

- ○ 40 hundreds 7 tens 4 ones   **procedural error**
- ○ $400 + 7 + 4$ **guess**
- ● four hundred seventy-four   **correct**
- ○ four seventy and four   **conceptual error**

3. Eliot has 4 pencils. Marco has 5 pencils. Lavonne has 6 pencils. How many pencils in all?

- ● 15 pencils   **correct**
- ○ 14 pencils   **guess**
- ○ 10 pencils   **procedural error**
- ○ 3 pencils   **conceptual error**

4. Justin makes 20 free throws. Tommy makes 17 free throws. Brian makes 14 free throws. How many free throws do they make in all?

- ○ 11   **procedural error**
- ○ 41   **procedural error**
- ○ 45   **guess**
- ● 51   **correct**

Grade 2   67   Chapter 12

12

Name _____

Cumulative Test Practice *(continued)*

**Read each question carefully.
Write your answer on the line.**

5.
$$34$$
$$\underline{-\ 6}$$
$$28$$

6. How many cents? **87** ¢

7. Count how many baseball there are. Write the answer as a number and number name.

12; twelve

8. How many faces does this figure have?

6 faces

9. A lunch box is 12 inches long. How many inches are in 4 lunch boxes?

48 inches

Grade 2   68   Chapter 12

STOP

Chapter Resources